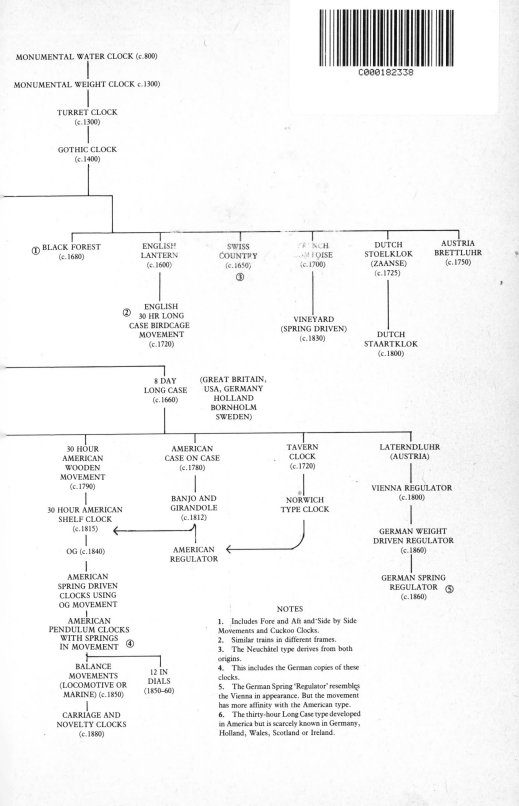

MONUMENTAL WATER CLOCK (c.800)

MONUMENTAL WEIGHT CLOCK c.1300)

TURRET CLOCK
(c.1300)

GOTHIC CLOCK
(c.1400)

① BLACK FOREST
(c.1680)

ENGLISH
LANTERN
(c.1600)

SWISS
COUNTRY
(c.1650)
③

FRENCH
COMTOISE
(c.1700)

DUTCH
STOELKLOK
(ZAANSE)
(c.1725)

AUSTRIA
BRETTLUHR
(c.1750)

② ENGLISH
30 HR LONG
CASE BIRDCAGE
MOVEMENT
(c.1720)

VINEYARD
(SPRING DRIVEN)
(c.1830)

DUTCH
STAARTKLOK
(c.1800)

8 DAY
LONG CASE
(c.1660)

(GREAT BRITAIN,
USA, GERMANY
HOLLAND
BORNHOLM
SWEDEN)

30 HOUR
AMERICAN
WOODEN
MOVEMENT
(c.1790)

AMERICAN
CASE ON CASE
(c.1780)

TAVERN
CLOCK
(c.1720)

LATERNDLUHR
(AUSTRIA)

30 HOUR AMERICAN
SHELF CLOCK
(c.1815)

BANJO AND
GIRANDOLE
(c.1812)

NORWICH
TYPE CLOCK

VIENNA REGULATOR
(c.1800)

OG (c.1840)

AMERICAN
REGULATOR

GERMAN WEIGHT
DRIVEN REGULATOR
(c.1860)

AMERICAN
SPRING DRIVEN
CLOCKS USING
OG MOVEMENT

GERMAN SPRING
REGULATOR ⑤
(c.1860)

AMERICAN
PENDULUM CLOCKS
WITH SPRINGS
IN MOVEMENT ④

BALANCE
MOVEMENTS
(LOCOMOTIVE OR
MARINE) (c.1850)

12 IN
DIALS
(1850–60)

CARRIAGE AND
NOVELTY CLOCKS
(c.1880)

NOTES

1. Includes Fore and Aft and Side by Side
Movements and Cuckoo Clocks.
2. Similar trains in different frames.
3. The Neuchâtel type derives from both
origins.
4. This includes the German copies of these
clocks.
5. The German Spring 'Regulator' resembles
the Vienna in appearance. But the movement
has more affinity with the American type.
6. The thirty-hour Long Case type developed
in America but is scarcely known in Germany,
Holland, Wales, Scotland or Ireland.

C000182338

Clock Types

Clock Types

E.J. TYLER

Longman
London and New York

Longman Group Limited
Longman House
Burnt Mill, Harlow, Essex, UK

*Published in the United States of America
by Longman Inc., New York*

©E. J. Tyler 1982

All rights reserved. No part of this publication
may be reproduced, stored in a retrieval
system, or transmitted in any form or by any
means, electronic, mechanical, photocopying,
recording, or otherwise, without the prior
permission of the Copyright owner.

First published 1982

British Library Cataloguing in Publication Data

Tyler, E. J.
  Clock types.
  1. Clocks and watches–History
  I. Title
  681.1'13'09   TS545

ISBN 0-582-50308-6

Library of Congress Cataloging in Publication Data

Tyler, E. J. (Eric John)
  Clock types.

  Bibliography: p.
  Includes index.
  1. Clocks and watches–Collectors and collecting.
I. Title.
NK484.T9   681.1'13'075   82–15358
ISBN 0-582-50308-6   AACR2

Printed in Great Britain at The Pitman Press, Bath

SHEFFIELD
C
682080996O
CITY
LIBRARIES
681
.113

Contents

Acknowledgements

The writer's thanks are due to the following who have assisted with illustrations:

Kingston Antiques,
Bill Matthews (Times Past),
Susan Lewis Antiques, St Leonards-on-Sea, Battle Tyme, Battle
and to a number of private collectors who wish to remain anonymous.

The publishers wish to acknowledge the work of Brian Jewell who helped prepare this book originally for the Midas Collectors' Library of which he was General Editor.

Introduction

The interest in clocks that has developed in recent years has meant that the types of clock formerly collected have been rising in price to the extent that the ordinary collector can no longer afford them. As a result other clock styles have been sought as collectable items, and there are so many on the market that the beginner may feel at a loss to know what clocks to collect.

If collecting is done for investment purposes only, then that is not true collecting. To get the most out of one's hobby the main aim should be to collect things that one likes and can live with, and the second requirement is that each piece should be understood by its owner who should have a clear idea of where the piece fits into the pattern of horological history.

This book has been written to help collectors with the second idea. Collecting now embraces such a wide field that every type cannot be listed, but a broad knowledge of the way that the clock has evolved and of the different contributions made to its development in various countries will provide a basis for further independent research. Half the fun of collecting is trying to add to the knowledge already available, and at the present time there is more help at the collector's disposal than ever before. During the last twenty years many of the American manufacturers' catalogues have been reproduced, and a considerable number of books have been written about various types of clock; a list of these has been included as an appendix.

Even if a collector wishes to specialise, a broad knowledge of the subject is helpful in studying his collection, and therefore books dealing with both high quality and cheaper models have been included in the list. Lists of makers are important for identification purposes and many of these are available but there is still a lot of work to be done in this field.

Membership of a society of enthusiasts is helpful not only for the personal contacts made but also for the society's publications which can, over a period of time, build up a sound knowledge of the subject. There are also periodicals on horology which are not related to any particular society and these can also be useful in providing knowledge.

Not every collector can do his own restoration but if it can be done it adds a great deal to the enjoyment of the hobby. Above all, it is not sufficient to read books and absorb what they contain. One has to do investigation of one's own and build up as much personal experience as possible.

Horology is essentially a sociable pastime and interesting discoveries are made by collaborating with other collectors. It is hoped that this book may be the means of giving would-be collectors some basic facts on which to start their careers and that they may go from strength to strength by means of further study and experience.

E.J.T.

1 *History of the Mechanical Clock*

It is not possible to say with certainty where or when or by whom the mechanical clock was invented. The latest available evidence suggests that there was a mechanical clock at Dunstable Priory in England as early as 1283, and other records have been discovered of clocks existing before 1300. During the 14th century the number increased and by 1400 the clock can be considered to have established itself as a part of everyday life.

The clock owes its origin to the need for knowing when to hold the numerous services during the day and night that formed such an important part of monastic life, but it was not long before it was used for secular purposes also. Cities would build a tower or 'Beffroi' as a status symbol and equip it with a clock which would announce the time to the citizens by striking one or more bells. Some places did not have the striking performed mechanically but would provide a smaller clock fitted with an alarm mechanism that would alert a watchman to ring a larger bell in a tower. The smaller type of clock has become well known from tarsia panels made in Italy which illustrate it, and it has been christened 'Monastic Alarm', showing that the practice was also carried out in monasteries as well as secular belfries. What is claimed to be the oldest of the smaller clocks is in the museum at Würzburg, Bavaria, and the suggested date is 1352.

It is generally accepted that the earliest clocks were the large type striking a bell in a tower, but some authorities maintain that the smaller type came first. Much more evidence is needed before any progress can be made with this problem, but it seems clear that by the beginning of the 15th century scaled down versions of the large clocks were being made for use in the home. They were naturally very expensive and their use was confined to only the richest citizens, but the important fact to be noted is that they were scaled down versions of the very large clocks rather than more complicated versions of the alarm type. Their frames were made of iron, decorated to suggest the tower in which the large

9

clock would have been placed; the striking work was placed behind the going mechanism, and the alarm work when fitted was of a more sophisticated type than that of the watchmen's clocks. These early domestic clocks, which are usually known by the name of 'Gothic Clocks', are extremely important in the history of timekeeping as many types have evolved from them, although their derivatives are today all but extinct as far as production is concerned.

The Gothic clock in its original basic form was in use from the 15th to the 17th century, although details changed as time went on. The history of this type can be studied by examining the products of one family, the Liechti family of Winterthur, Switzerland, whose clocks are found in many museums as well as in the Kellenberger Collection in Winterthur itself. Many generations of the Liechti family were clockmakers and they were unusual for their period in that they signed their work.

The clocks were all driven by weights to begin with and were controlled by a balance, either a 'foliot' consisting of a horizontal arm with two small weights on it that could be moved towards or away from the centre to regulate the clock, or else a wheel sometimes in the form of a plain ring or sometimes decorated like a crown. The disadvantage of this method was that the balance had no definite period of swing of its own and the timekeeping of the clock could be affected by a change in the driving force as the primitive teeth took up new positions in relation to each other, or by changes in the consistency of the oil, ingress of dirt, etc. The clock might be fast or slow of the correct time at different periods of the day.

The Gothic clock was essentially a European production. There were examples in England; for instance, we know that Sir Thomas More possessed one, but the making of clocks by Englishmen was scarcely known before 1600 and all clocks used in the country before then would have been imported, except in rare instances. The large tower clocks were made in England, but in most cases by workmen from the Continent.

The Gothic clock necessarily had to hang on the wall or be supported by a pillar on account of the weights. The next development was to drive the clock by means of a spring to render it portable. It was formerly believed that the spring only came into use about 1500 but recent discoveries have shown that it was in use before this date. The oldest spring clock is generally claimed to be that belonging to Philip the Good, Duke of Burgundy, now in the Germanisches Museum at Nuremberg, and a date of c1430 is suggested. There is, however, doubt about this clock although some evidence has been brought to confirm its date. The wheels are of iron and gilded and the winding is by means of tiny capstans instead of a key.

The use of the mainspring brought new problems and its development was somewhat retarded. The making of a thin ribbon of steel that could be wound and unwound an infinite number of times without breaking was an achievement in itself, and as a spring exerts more force when nearly wound up than it does when nearly run down, it would affect the rate of the clock if steps were not taken to compensate for this. The usual method is by means of a 'fusee' which can be likened to a truncated cone with a spiral groove cut on its surface. The spring is contained in a drum called a barrel and the fusee and barrel are connected by a gut line. When the clock is run down, all the line is wound round the surface of the barrel and the clock is wound by rotating the fusee and coiling the line on it. As the line comes off the barrel it causes it to rotate and so wind the spring. When the clock is fully wound, the spring is pulling that part of the line which is on the smallest groove of the fusee and as the spring unwinds further the line is pulling on a groove of larger diameter, thereby working with a more favourable leverage. With the verge escapement that was universally used in the early days of clockwork, this helped to reduce errors arising from variations in power.

There was another type of power equaliser known as the 'stackfreed', which was a friction brake working on a shaped cam, but although ingenious, this was not particularly efficient, and did not have a long life. It seems to have been applied mostly in Germany.

One of the oldest known illustrations of a spring clock appears in the corner of a portrait of a Burgundian nobleman. The picture was painted about 1460 possibly by Rogier van der Weyden, and the clock is shaped like a normal Gothic wall clock but has a small length of chain attached to the top. The springs in their barrels are contained in the base and the fusees and the wheels are arranged above them as on the Philip the Good clock.

Much more definite evidence about clocks with springs is provided by a manuscript written by a German monk, Paulus Almanus, who spent a number of years in Rome from 1475. He described a number of clocks he had seen belonging to various officials and a number of these were spring driven.

The next development was arranging all the wheels and mechanism between two plates instead of between strips of metal fitted into a 'birdcage' type of frame. The earliest precedent for this is in a manuscript in the Bibliotheque Royale in Brussels which shows a large clock and other time measuring instruments. On the table of the room is what appears to be a clock movement with a fusee contained between a pair of plates. With this arrangement the striking train and going train are side by side instead of end to end. The importance of this development will be seen as the story continues. Most types of clock directly derived from the 'Gothic' arrangement have ceased to be produced, but such mechanical clocks as are made today all have the plate type of movement. The latter is more compact, simpler to manufacture and stronger. In the earliest times when it was made, one of the biggest problems was the production of the plates themselves, but by the beginning of the 18th century, or even earlier, the plate movement was well established.

The important development of the mid-16th century was the use of brass instead of iron. The alloy is easier to work, and when brass wheels are used in conjunction with steel pinions there is less friction than when both are of the same metal.

Some very small clocks were made in the early 16th century that were small enough to be carried on the person and therefore can be considered the first watches, but they were of iron and these small machines would have benefitted greatly from the use of brass.

After the plate movement had been adopted, the spring driven clock could be made in a square or drum shaped case which would protect the movement from dust and interference. The Gothic clocks had their movement exposed, and what decoration there was had to be on the columns of the framework or applied to the dial by paint. When the movement could be shut up in a box, the box itself could be the subject for decoration and one sees many such clock cases engraved and gilded.

An early function of the larger clocks was to give astronomical indications and, in effect, represent a model of the universe. In the Middle Ages, the telling of the hours of the day was of less importance than showing the position of the Heavenly Bodies, and these elaborate clocks were often set up in cathedrals as an illustration of the power of the Almighty in creating and controlling the universe. With the spring driven table clock these astronomical indications appeared again, firstly because there were a number of educated people who took an interest in astronomy and would find such a clock useful, while others would simply need them as a status symbol.

The Copernican Theory appeared in the mid-16th century and by the end of that century astronomy was being studied more scientifically.

Astronomers needed more accurate time measurement devices to assist in their observations and the clocks available at that time were of little use. A Swiss clockmaker named Jost Burgi devised a new escapement that was a great improvement on the existing verge escapement and constructed several clocks with it which can be seen at Kassel and Vienna. The cutting of the teeth of the wheels of these clocks shows what a high standard of workmanship had been achieved at that time and the new escapement was a vast improvement on what had been done before. It worked on the principle of two much lighter foliots coupled together so that they moved in opposite directions. A slight springiness in the arms may have helped, but the escapement still had no definite period, and although an improvement, was not capable of permitting the clock to be called a precision instrument.

The clock as a precision instrument only evolved when the pendulum was applied to clockwork, for a pendulum has a definite period of swing which is determined by its length. A number of men were working on the idea in the early 17th century, and the pioneer is usually considered to be the Italian scientist Galileo who left a description of a pendulum clock which, however, was not made in his lifetime. A German clockmaker named Johann Philipp Treffler, working in Italy was also experimenting with the idea, but the man who first managed to design a successful pendulum clock was the Dutch scientist Christiaan Huygens. Huygens completed his experimental model on Christmas Day 1656 and, in 1657, was granted a patent by the States General. The clocks were made by a clockmaker in The Hague named Salomon Coster, and it is important to note that Coster was a maker of table clocks which had plate movements and the earliest pendulum clocks had this type of movement and were spring driven. The confidence felt in the new design was so great that the fusee was done away with and the barrel was provided with teeth that drove the movement direct.

The verge or spindle that carries the two pallets in the verge escapement has to move through quite a large angle to unlock, and therefore a pendulum on such a clock must have a wide swing. This means that the pendulum can only be short. The advantage of a long pendulum is that with a slight movement of the bob it is possible to effect a very small adjustment of the rate, whereas the same movement of the bob on a short pendulum would involve a much greater difference in rate. The problem of applying a longer pendulum was only solved in the early 1670s by the invention of the anchor escapement. With this the pendulum needs to move only a few degrees to unlock, and this means that the clock can be provided with a comparatively narrow case. The anchor escapement brought another advantage; Huygens had discovered that a pendulum will take the same time to swing through a long or a short arc only if the bob moves through a curve known as a cycloid. The bob of a pendulum normally describes part of a circle, but when the amplitude of the swing is very small, the difference between the cycloid and the circle is too little to give concern. Huygens suspended his pendulums on threads and guided the movement of the threads by special cheeks which turned out to be more bother than they were worth, and so clockmakers were glad enough to use the long pendulum and forget the cheeks.

The application of the pendulum meant that the indication of minutes at last had a meaning. Previously the shortest interval that could be measured was the half-quarter or 7½ minutes. Huygens was also responsible for placing the minute hand concentric with the hour hand and his earliest type of clock was very modern in appearance. At first, every minute was numbered, then only every five, later every ten, and, after limiting the numbers to every quarter of an hour, minute numbers disappeared early in the 19th century. Some clocks have been made with them since, but that is a matter for the designer. By the late 19th century even the hour figures were being shown by strokes and this is still seen on clocks and watches made today.

The 18th century saw further attempts to obtain higher precision. Differences in temperature make a pendulum change its length and this can have a marked effect on the timekeeping, a clock tending to gain in cold weather and lose when it is warmer. This problem was tackled in the early 18th century by John Harrison who arranged a number of brass and steel rods which expanded or contracted in such a way that the position of the bob remained the same; this is known as The 'Gridiron' pendulum.

The famous London clockmaker George Graham invented the mercury pendulum, where the bob consists of a jar of mercury the quantity being so adjusted that the downward expansion of the pendulum rod is exactly compensated for by the expansion and rise of the mercury in the jar. Another London clockmaker, Ellicott, also produced a compensation device where the downward expansion of two rods acted on levers which raised the bob. This method has not found much application in Britain but has appeared on a number of French clocks.

Graham also invented the 'dead beat' escapement which does away with recoil and gives excellent results.

14

Later developments in the 18th century were nearly all in connection with telling the time at sea. Harrison was the pioneer of producing an accurate marine timekeeper, and his improvements to clocks were an attempt to provide an accurate standard by which to test his marine timekeepers. Harrison produced three large machines for use at sea which could be called clocks, but finally turned his attention to a very large watch, and it was this design which led to subsequent developments in marine timekeeping.

The 19th-century developments in clockmaking were more concerned with changes in manufacture rather than new inventions. France and the USA both began the making of clocks in factories quite early in the century, and Germany and Austria followed suit later. After 1873 several attempts were made to establish clock factories in Japan but it took some time before this was successful.

Perhaps one of the most important results of the change over to factory production was the increased popularity of the cheap clock controlled by a balance instead of a pendulum. These clocks were of course provided with balance springs (hairsprings) but their great advantage was that they were portable and did not need accurate setting up every time they were placed on a new surface. They were also made with metal cases, another instance of history repeating itself, and these were cheaper and simpler than wooden cases. The ordinary alarm clock is a product of the third quarter of the 19th century and the same basic movement has been used in a variety of cases, some even of black marble.

The 20th century saw little further development in the mechanical clock but is noteworthy for the development of the electric clock, both mains and battery driven. Electric clocks are beginning to be considered collectors' items but the subject is too vast to be treated here.

The foregoing is a very broad outline of the development of the mechanical clock, and details in the story will be filled in as various countries in Europe and Scandinavia are considered. The history of clock development in USA is quite different from that in Europe; the products of American factories found a ready market in Europe and other parts of the world and their story is an important part of horological evolution in general. It was to influence production in both Germany and Japan with subsequent developments in Britain.

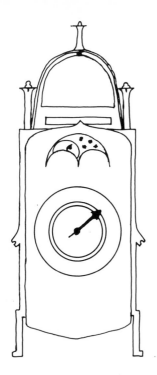

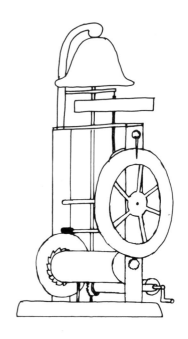

The earliest Gothic wall clocks were tall and slender, suggesting the towers in which public clocks were placed.

The monastic alarm was a primitive time piece. This example shows the time by a rotating dial. The small crank at the bottom is for winding the alarm mechanism.

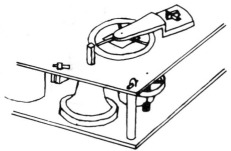

The earliest table clocks had their movements arranged between plates, and this was to have far reaching effects on clock design in later years.

An example of a square cased table clock. The slots on the side of the case are for letting the sound of the bell escape.

16

The drum type table clock was neater and led the way to the production of watches. The small door is for the purpose of inspecting the fusee to see if the clock required winding.

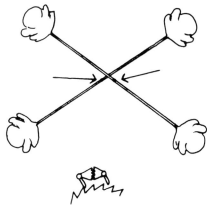

The Cross Beat Escapement. The arrows point to the centres about which the arms are rotating. These centres are normally covered by a small plate and there is an optical illusion that both the arms are on the same centre. The lower sketch shows how the scapewheel impels the pallets which are connected by gearing.

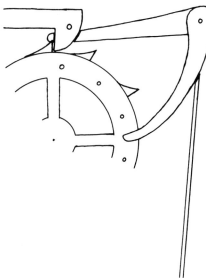

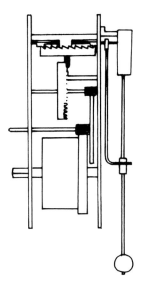

Galileo's Escapement. As the pendulum swings to the left the comma shaped piece touches one of the pins in the rim of the wheel and causes a recoil. The horizontal arm raises the hook at the top of the wheel and allows the wheel to turn. As it does so it impulses the pendulum through the pin pressing on the comma piece and the hook is allowed to descend and lock the wheel once more.

The arrangement of the movement of the early pendulum clocks. Apart from the verge escapement and the cheeks to guide the pendulum suspension, the layout is completely modern.

17

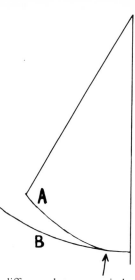

The difference between a circle and a cycloid. (A) shows the cycloid which is steeper than the circular path (B), and the arrow shows the extent of the swing of a pendulum using an anchor escapement where the cycloid and the circle are so nearly equal that the difference does not matter.

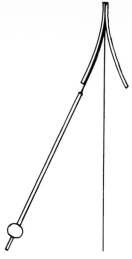

A pendulum guided by cycloidal cheeks. Many early makers did not understand the principle correctly and the cheeks they used are not made to the correct shape. The pendulum is hung on a pair of long flexible threads which wrap themselves along the surface of the cheeks.

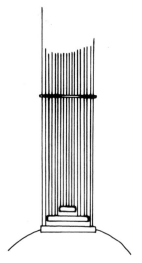

A gridiron pendulum. The rods are alternately brass and steel, and are calculated so that the expansion of one set is counteracted exactly by that of the other.

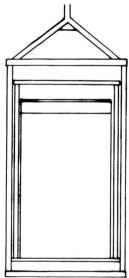

A mercury compensation. The bob of the pendulum is formed of a stirrup supporting a jar of mercury. The amount of mercury is arranged so that its upward expansion when the temperature rises exactly compensates for the downward expansion of the pendulum rod.

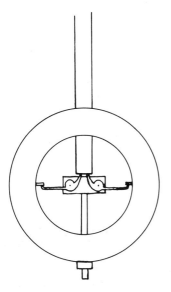

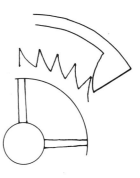

The Anchor Escapement. When a tooth strikes a pallet the motion of the latter continues for an instant and the wheel is forced to recoil.

Ellicott's compensation. A brass rod fixed to the pendulum rod expands downwards in heat and pushes on the ends of two small levers which raise the bob.

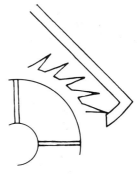

The Dead Beat Escapement. The pallet face on which the tooth strikes is a circle with its centre at the centre about which the pallets are rotating and there is therefore no recoil.

2 *National Characteristics*

In tracing the evolution of the clock through various countries, our task can be summarised as recording the development of the two types of movement, the 'birdcage' type used in the Gothic clock and the plate type used in the table clock. Clocks are essentially classified by their movements, the case and decoration being only of secondary importance in this connection.

BRITAIN

There were virtually no British clockmakers before the end of the Elizabethan era. Henry VIII and Elizabeth I had large numbers of clocks in their possession, but all these would have been imported or produced by foreign workmen resident in this country. Some of the latter may have only been in this country for a short time and others may have settled here, but the truly British clock was not produced in quantity until the early years of the 17th century when British craftsmen had had time to learn from Continental immigrants.

The earliest type of British clock was a development of the Gothic wall clock, but the movement was mainly of brass instead of iron. The movement was also enclosed by sheet brass doors which represented an important improvement over the original design. In the mid-16th century brass production had been encouraged in the North of England and a number of German workers had been brought over to develop the industry.

Most of the technical terms in use in clockmaking at the time were French, and many survive today; as the French word for brass is 'Laiton', the new type of clock would be known as a 'Laiton' clock which would have been rendered as 'Lantern' by the English.

The forged iron pillars on the prototype were replaced by turned brass ones, and the tall slender shape of the Gothic clock was replaced by something less tall in proportion to its width. The bell was larger and contributed to the outline of the clock. The earliest examples were balance controlled, but so far all evidence points to the exclusive use of the wheel balance and no British clocks with a foliot have been recorded. The wheel balance is plain in contrast to the decorated examples of the Continent, for on the British clocks the balance would be hidden by decorative frets. Many balance clocks were converted to pendulum control after 1660 and some collectors and dealers who possess such clocks have had them altered back to balance in recent years. A conversion to pendulum is easy to detect because the old holes for the balance cock and other parts have usually been left, but when the reconversion has been done attempts are often made to hide the fact that a conversion has taken place and one should be on the alert for holes stopped with brass of a different colour and any other significant clues. It is extremely rare to find a clock that has not been converted, and one which appears to be in its original condition should be treated with suspicion.

The earliest lantern clocks had a single hand with a tail which helped when setting the clock to time, and the chapter ring was very narrow. As the 17th century progressed, the chapter ring became broader and projected further beyond the case. By the early 18th century, the dials were often square and approximated to the dials of long case clocks.

An early lantern clock represented the height of fashion and would have been made by a man in a large city such as London, Norwich or Edinburgh. After the introduction of the pendulum, the new spring driven clocks with wooden cases and the long case clock became popular and the lantern clock became mostly a country production. Exceptions to this rule were small lantern clocks which were meant to be taken on journeys and put up on the wall of an inn bedroom for the night. These clocks are usually fitted with alarm only. Examples survive which were made by leading London makers such as Tompion and Graham who flourished when the lantern clock was becoming unfashionable as a domestic timekeeper.

The period for converting lantern clocks was generally 1660-1700 and new clocks made during that period were provided at first with the short pendulum and a verge escapement. Later a long pendulum and anchor escapement were used and the lantern clock gradually evolved into a cheaper kind of movement for a long case clock. The brass dial with a single hand lasted until about 1750; then a brass dial with two hands, and after about 1780 a painted iron dial, which continued to be provided until the making of these clocks ceased about 1870-80. The brass dials used in the early 18th century would have possessed separate brass chapter rings, cast spandrels and matted centres.

The single hand would have been of steel and retained its tail for assisting in setting to time, but with the advent of the two handed dial the hands would have been more delicate and corresponded to the hands used on eight day long case clocks at the time. It is correct for the separate chapter ring to be silvered as this makes a contrast for the steel hands, which should be blued. Many silvered chapter rings have worn with the years and most people accept the polished brass surface as normal.

With the painted iron dial there also developed a brass dial which was engraved and meant to be silvered, but these dials are mostly found today with the silvering worn off.

The plain silvered dial is very attractive but was more expensive than a painted one and therefore could not compete with it. Until recently it was considered that a painted dial was worthless and also that a thirty hour clock was not a collectable item. Consequently much butchering has taken place; eight day clocks have had their painted dials replaced by brass ones, and thirty hour clocks with brass dials have had eight day movements fitted. This involves drilling holes for the insertion of the key in the matted centre of the dial, and if the clock originally had a single hand there will be no minute marks, which were always found on two handed clocks in the brass dial period, usually with each fifth minute numbered in Arabic figures.

This state of affairs arose because people followed the dictates of fashion and the trade acted accordingly. Nowadays collectors are beginning to realise that the painted iron dial can have a beauty of its own, and the price of all antique clocks offered for sale is so high that one would hesitate to do any adaption. Even the daily winding of a thirty hour clock is discovered to be a less onerous task than was feared.

The lantern clock is a text book case of the development of the Gothic type of movement to suit local taste; it eventually ceased to be produced as a result of competition from other types of clock. The first competition was from the new pendulum clock from Holland which came to London about the time of the Restoration of Charles II in 1660. The end of the Commonwealth and its austerity created a demand for new and gayer items of furniture in houses, and these small spring driven clocks with their wooden cases were eagerly accepted. They were, however, expensive; in effect a development of the Continental table clock with a plate movement and spring drive which had been seen and even made in

Britain but was not so popular as the lantern clock. David Ramsay, the first Master of the Clockmakers' Company made this type of clock for which his French training had admirably suited him and other London makers also produced it, but national taste wanted something more solid. This was demonstrated when the wooden cased spring clock began to be made in London. The Dutch prototypes had very small movements and dispensed with fusees, but the British clockmakers preferred to use the latter and to make the movement much larger so that it filled the case. This characteristic of large movements, solidly made, continued until the late 19th century when the last hand-made clocks of the traditional type were produced.

The making of springs was still a difficult task in the 17th century, and it was not long after the introduction of the pendulum that the new type of movement was produced with a weight drive. The short pendulum was retained, but the fusees were replaced with grooved barrels on which were wound gut lines. The outer end of the line was fastened to the seat board of the movement and the weights were suspended from pulleys supported by the resulting loops. The wooden cases were made in the architectural style and veneered with ebony.

In the past it has been believed that these clocks were first produced with cases that covered the movement only and allowed the weights to be seen. The pendulum was, of course, too short to be visible outside the case. The exposed weights were not considered elegant and consequently were encased in a narrow cupboard and hence the long case clock was born. Today it is believed that the hooded clock and the long case clock grew up together and the one did not develop from the other. Clocks with a hood only of this period are very rare. The driving weights put a considerable load on the support, and a long case is a much more satisfactory way of supporting the clock than hanging it on the wall.

In the 18th century many thirty hour movements were supplied with hooded brackets, especially the smaller ones that had time and alarm only. On a clock of this type the driving weight is less, and consequently the problem of load is less acute.

Early long case movements are easily recognisable for they are usually tall, have very large main wheels with the rest of the train consisting of wheels which are extremely small in comparison, the pillars are often of the balustrade type and are secured by latches instead of pins. There are often more than the four necessary to hold the plates together. The striking is controlled by a count wheel placed high on the back plate. Dials are only about 23cm (9in) square and have separate chapter rings with short figures. The spandrels are very simple, usually consisting of a cherub's head.

Introduction of the anchor escapement, with its long pendulum, meant that the trunk of the case had to be wider, and, in order to keep the balance of design, the dial and hood had to be larger as well. With this increase in size, the architectural style of the case gave way to cases decorated with veneer and later, especially during the reign of William and Mary, the use of marquetry was very popular. The making of marquetry was a speciality of Dutch craftsmen and its use in Britain was an outward sign of the fusion of the Ruling Houses of England and Holland. During the late 17th century the long case clock usually had twisted pillars flanking the dial, the case stood on bun feet and there was a carved crest on top of the hood. The crests and feet have mostly disappeared from the clocks seen today.

Dials became larger, being made up to 30cm (12in) and the chapter rings became wider with more engraving applied, consisting of elaborate half-hour marks between the hour figures and quarter-hour marks inside the figures. The winding holes were covered by shutters which did not permit the clock to be wound until a cord had been pulled to open them; the operation compressed a spring and provided extra power to keep the clock going while winding was taking place. In the early years of the 18th century the maintaining power came to be fitted less; the holes were often surrounded by engraved rings which may have been intended to protect the matted surface of the dial centre from the winding key.

Dials were square until about 1720 after which the arched dial became fashionable. The earliest dial had the arch fastened separately, but later dials were made in one piece, and by about 1730-40 the arch might accommodate a disc for showing the phases of the moon or a moving figure such as a rocking ship.

As the 18th century progressed, the difference in sizes of the wheels became less marked and pillars tended to become plainer. The use of latches for fastening plates gave way to tapered pins and by the end of the century the five or more pillars had been generally reduced to four.

It is now beginning to be accepted that the name on the dial of a long case clock is not that of the man who made it. Tompion is believed to have possessed a factory where rough movements were produced which were finished in his workshop at Water Lane, Blackfriars, to individual customers' requirements. From the end of the 17th century the clockmakers were able to buy partly prepared material for speeding up the task of constructing movements. Some clockmakers engraved their own dials, others had the work done for them by specialists, and after the introduction of the painted dial about 1770 dials were generally produced by specialist manufacturers, mostly in Birmingham, the name of the 'maker' being painted on after delivery. Large orders could mean that the name was painted on at the dialmaker's. By the end of the 18th century it was possible to order a finished movement to be attached to a ready made dial; the 'clockmaker' had nothing to do but order from his suppliers. But still the local man had to use discrimination as to what he bought, and by putting his name on the dial he was taking responsibility for the finished product. He could be sure that if anything went wrong the owner would know where to return the clock. Also, at this time it was much cheaper to order finished movements rather than make them. Had individual work been necessary, the price would have resulted in the demand being much smaller.

There are, of course, the exceptions to this. In very isolated villages the local man would still be making movements himself, but even such movements as these are to be seen with Birmingham made dials.

An offshoot of the long case clock was the 'Act of Parliament' or 'Tavern' clock. Legend has it that these were produced in 1797 after the Government had put a tax on clocks and watches, but the type was well known throughout the 18th century. Their chief function was to show the time in large rooms, such as in a tavern, so that everyone would know how long the wait would be before the next coach started. Coaches were run to very strict timetables. Tavern clocks have large dials and were hung on the wall so that the dial was at a higher level than that of the long case type; the movement needed adaptation so that the eight day period of running could be maintained with the weight falling through a smaller distance. The earliest clocks of this type had dials unglazed, but later dials became smaller and were covered with a glass that was often convex. The smaller dial variety is associated with East Anglia and called the 'Norwich Type', but these clocks were made in other parts of the country as well. A 19th-century development of the type adorned many railway stations.

During the 17th—19th centuries, Britain was the world leader of horological production, but British makers refused to take notice of the Industrial Revolution and competition from overseas eventually destroyed the horological trade in this country. Cheap clocks had first come from the Black Forest and, after 1842, these had been supplanted on the British market by imports from America. Later in the century the Black Forest went over to factory production and regained the ground formerly lost to America. During the 1850s Sir John Bennett, a well known London horologist was drawing attention to the situation, and the British Horological Institute was formed in 1858 to help the Trade with its problems, but still old methods prevailed and by 1900 British horology was well on the way out. The long case clock was still made in Wales up to about 1880, but that was the end. Clerkenwell workshops could still produce solid bracket clocks with quarter chimes in the Edwardian era, but similar German made clocks were being sold for half the price. The factory-made French circular movement with a pendulum was produced in thousands and sold in Britain in the black marble cases so beloved by the Victorians. This French movement is one of the best things ever done commercially, and it is a pity that the marble cases usually make them unpopular today.

One type of British clock did however survive and was made until a few years ago when the electric clock began to take over. This was the 'English Dial', a wall clock usually having a dial 30cm (12in) in diameter and possessing a movement of the traditional British type with a fusee. These clocks were usually timepieces only but were found in a great variety of places where it was necessary for the time to be seen by a large number of people: offices, schools, hospitals, railway stations, shops, restaurants, etc. They are now being regarded as collectors' items and a book has recently been published on them. It is perhaps surprising to learn that this typical 19th-century product was already being made in the 18th century, and that some of the earlier examples were very attractive indeed. These clocks were also produced in Germany, even with the fusee.

The same movement that was used for the English Dial also appeared in the skeleton clock, which had most of its plates cut away in decorated forms and was covered by a glass shade. These clocks were very popular in Victorian times and were produced in factories, although an idea seems to be circulating that they were made by apprentices as a masterpiece when they had completed their training. There seems to be no reason for this belief.

Clock production in Britain today is concerned with the smaller types as far as most factories are concerned. Alarm clocks, novelty and travelling clocks are produced, but a limited amount of factory work of higher quality is undertaken. Replicas of older types are very popular, the skeleton clock having been chosen by several makers, and clocks based on the 18th-century bracket clocks are also made. There are some smaller factories that specialise in getting closer to the traditional product but their output is, of necessity, limited. Some firms supply clocks in cases based on traditional designs but use imported movements.

The characteristic of the British movement was always its solidity and high finish. It contained far more metal than was necessary to do the job, but these characteristics have made the British clock a highly desirable collector's item. The modern reproductions are generally forced to contain less raw material for economic reasons, and while this does not necessarily impair their efficiency as timekeepers, it distinguishes them from the products of earlier years.

HOLLAND

The history of horology in Holland is remarkable in that it broadly consisted of a local development of the Gothic movement which continued from the early 17th century to the late 19th, and yet cutting across this was the greatest improvement in time measurement known for centuries. The pendulum clocks produced by Dutch makers as a result of the work of Christiaan Huygens influenced clockmaking in France and Britain, and yet after a few years the Dutch were content to rest on their laurels and during the 18th century were copying the British eight day long case clock; at the end of the century they were looking to France for inspiration. The home produced clock of Dutch design was made mainly in the country districts and eventually succumbed to the cheaper and more sophisticated clocks from German factories.

It was not that talent was lacking. As early as the 14th century, Edward III of England was giving his official protection to three 'Orologiers' from Delft who were to exercise their craft in the realm. By the early 17th century the Dutch turret clock was a very advanced piece of mechanism, and as early as 1544 the Old Church at Amsterdam was provided with a dial on each side of the tower. Many of the early turret clocks in Holland were arranged to play carillons and some of these performed every seven-and-a-half minutes. The wheels of the clocks were large and the clocks had very large scapewheels with numerous teeth which helped to steady the erratic action of the foliot.

Up to the middle of the 17th century the Gothic wall clock was not very different from examples made in other parts of Europe, but then there developed a tendency to house these in wooden cases, and in the province of North Holland, especially round Zaandam, there were so many made that it was possible to consider them as belonging to a distinctive type which was known as the Zaandam or Zaanse clock. The movements were made of brass instead of iron and the wheels were decorated, possessing bifurcated crossings usually seen in the turret clocks. Unlike the original pendulum clocks, the pendulum was much longer than the movement and hung in a decorated box at the rear which formed part of the clock case. The weights were supported on an endless cord on the system devised by Huygens and were usually pear shaped with a polished brass finish. The large bell on the top of the clock was surmounted by a statuette, sometimes of Minerva but generally of Atlas holding the world.

The Zaanse clock was made c1670 to 1720 and by that time was succeeded by the English type of long case clock, which was produced by a number of makers in many of the larger Dutch towns. Before we consider them in detail it is necessary to have a look at the earliest type of pendulum clock made to Huygens' design, and as they were first produced in The Hague they are known as 'Haagse Klokjes'.

What Salomon Coster did when he constructed the pioneer pendulum clock was to make a table clock movement and turn it on its side so that the scapewheel came on top. The short pendulum hung at the rear and the fusee and separate barrel were replaced by a going barrel, i.e. one with teeth round the edge driving the mechanism direct. The dial was a metal plate covered with black velvet and the chapter ring of silver formed a good contrast to its background. The whole was contained in a comparatively plain wooden case. Later the cases of these clocks were provided with decoration. The same type was also produced in France after Huygens went to live there, but while the design died out in Holland and was replaced by long case clocks or spring driven clocks based on English models which had developed from the original Dutch design, in France the type was developed out of all recognition to become the large and elaborate clocks of the Louis XV period.

It is believed that the English long case clock was introduced to Holland by Joseph Norris who worked in Amsterdam. The earliest he made were very similar to the English models, but as time went on the Dutch clock tended to show more elaboration. Marquetry lasted longer than in England and the Dutch clock usually had elaboration of the dial with automata or showing the days of the week. Automata and music were very popular and, in contrast to English clocks, the space between the movement and dial was often crowded with mechanism. Much of the material was provided from London, and a distinction between Dutch and English dials is that on an English clock the minute figures are gradually turning as they proceed round the dial until the 30 at six o'clock is upside down, while on a Dutch dial the 20 at four o'clock is reversed and 30 is upright.

While the long case clock was popular in the towns, in country places a wall clock known as a 'Stoelklok' was made. This was a development of the Gothic clock but the frame was composed of brass uprights, with sheet iron plates at top and bottom. The verge escapement was used with the scapewheel vertical, and a wire went from the top of the verge to engage with the pendulum which was hung from the back of the bracket. The striking was of a primitive type, released when a lever had been lifted to a certain height. This is not so exact as the normal type of striking which 'warns' a few minutes before the hour and then is released by a falling lever. The brackets were painted in bright colours and often flanked with mermaids or other decoration. The dials of the clocks were also painted in bright colours and had cast lead ornaments at the sides and top which might be gilded or decorated with paint. The whole clock was surmounted with a canopy that protected it from dust and which also bore some gilded or painted lead ornamentation.

The Stoelklok is usually associated with the province of Friesland, but it was also made in other parts of the Netherlands, the style usually giving away the place of origin. In the East of the country some even had the anchor escapement. This led to the next development in the country clock which came in about 1800. An anchor escapement was used on the original type of movement and the pendulum was longer, being about 80cm. It was contained in a polished wooden box at the rear, as on the Zaanse clock, and a small window allowed the bob to be seen so that one could be certain that the clock was still going. The movement was enclosed in a hood, as on the long case clock, and the dial, of the arched type, also resembled the long case style. The weight and chain were visible, hanging straight down from the movement and not boxed in.

The new type of clock was known as a 'Staartklok' (Tail clock) and was made until about 1880, when German factory products had driven it off the market. Particularly pleasing are the smaller versions with a total length of about 1m, which are known as a 'Kantoorklok' or office clock.

Both the Stoelklok and the Staartklok were made in miniature versions for use on the vessels that traversed the inland waterways of the Netherlands. They were fitted with verge escapements having a horizontal verge and a tiny pendulum which moved very rapidly and was tolerant of changes in level as the vessel rolled. These clocks were known as 'Schippertjes' and are very highly prized by collectors today.

At the end of the 18th century fashion in Holland changed and French clock styles were adopted. The national styles lingered on in the country but were finished before the end of the 19th century. It seems a pity that the country that gave the world the pendulum clock, and which was a leader in the early days of the turret clock, should have had so little influence elsewhere in the history of horology.

FRANCE

For centuries France has enjoyed a high reputation for horology. A clock was installed at Paris in 1370 by Henri de Vic and the oldest clock in existence with quarter chimes is that of Rouen, made in 1389. France seems to have had less interest in the Gothic wall clock than Germany, but after the introduction of the mainspring the spring driven clock became a French speciality. Louis XI (1461-83) possessed at least one spring driven clock and during the 16th century the making of clocks in France reached a high level. The first Guild of Clockmakers in Paris was incorporated in 1544 and the influence of France on horology can be seen today in the number of French words used by horologists, e.g. Remontoir, Fusee.

A speciality of French makers was a table clock in tower form where the trains of wheels were contained between horizontal plates one above the other.

French makers were producing large numbers of watches in the late 16th century, and the clock, apart from the table clock which French makers liked to make small, did not enjoy great popularity. After the introduction of the Haagse Klokje in Holland and the subsequent arrival of Huygens in Paris, where he lived for a number of years, French makers began producing very close copies of the Dutch model, but as the years went by the original plain appearance became more and more decorated and the clock underwent a change that made it unrecognisable from the prototype. The rectangular case was enlarged and straight lines replaced by curves. Carving and gilding were applied together with cast bronze ornaments, dials were made with enamel, firstly using plaques on account of difficulty in manufacture and later making the dials in one piece. The clocks of the Dutch style were named 'Religieuse' (Nun) on account of their austere appearance and this name is also applied to the early developments which are less austere but retain the rectangular case. Sometimes the name Louis XIII is also used but these clocks were not introduced until after his reign.

The developments of the spring driven clock included more glass at the front so that the pendulum could be seen, but in the early days a plain bob was usual. Many clocks are seen today with a sunburst pendulum suggesting Le Roi Soleil, but this is not correct, the sunburst pendulum being a later addition to these clocks.

Towards the middle of the 18th century the Rococo style came in and everything had to be asymmetric. Winding holes were given asymmetric placing in the dial which meant a modification of the movement. The Cartel clock was popular and this allowed decoration at the base as well, as the clock did not have to stand but hung on the wall. In the reign of Louis XVI classical styles for clock cases were introduced and there was a tendency for clocks to become smaller again. Arabic figures also made their appearance and started a fashion that spread to Britain and USA. Statuettes, particularly Venus and Cupid, became popular. The Revolutionary period brought in much plainer styles, roughly corresponding with the Regency period in Britain, and the Egyptian campaign of Napoleon gave inspiration for clock cases with Egyptian motifs.

Napoleon's military campaigns gave rise to a type of clock known as a 'Pendule d'Officier' which was for the use of officers on active service. These clocks are circular, in metal cases and often have striking with repetition and alarm work — an elaborate version of the modern alarm clock. A certain amount of decoration was applied to the metal case and the movement was also decorated. As the clocks had to be portable, balance control was necessary, and in fact the whole clock could be regarded as a large watch with complications.

Another type of French clock seen about this time was the 'Capucine', named after the Capucine nuns on account of its plainness. The case is of brass and is rectangular with a plain circular white dial and a bell on the top as on an English lantern clock. These clocks have been seen with both balance and pendulum control and were made in various sizes.

The firm of Japy Frères began producing movements under factory conditions in 1810. They were the pioneers of French movements which were exported in enormous numbers later in the century. A popular style of clock bearing this type of movement, which had circular plates, was the Portico clock, usually known today simply as Empire, where four pillars support an entablature from which the movement is hung. Usually such a clock has a gridiron pendulum. During the Second Empire many replicas of the older styles were made, but they are usually recognisable by their circular movements and machine-made screws in the case.

The long case clock did not enjoy the popularity in France that it had in other countries. When they were made they were usually precision clocks designed for the maximum accuracy, and often, surprisingly, included Huygens' continuous rope drive which has the advantage of keeping the clock going while winding without separate maintaining power.

The comparative unpopularity of the long case clock only refers to the products of the large towns. In the country the Comtoise clock was popular and many of these were placed in long cases made by local craftsmen, which may suggest that the entire clock is locally made, whereas in fact the movements were all produced in the Jura, the district known as Franche Comté (hence Comtoise) and especially in Morbier or Morez which provide alternative names for the type.

The Comtoise was the French development of the Gothic movement, although the trains were placed side by side and not one behind the other. The frame was of steel or iron and the clock was provided with sheet iron doors to the frame excluding dust and allowing the clock to be hung on the wall as an independent unit. The clocks were factory produced even though outworkers were involved. Movements were dispatched to all parts of France and were usually marked with the name of the vendor, after which the customer had a case made or hung the clock on the wall as desired. The long cases for the Comtoise clocks are usually made broader at the part where the pendulum bob is accommodated, a feature also often seen on more expensive types.

The Comtoise dial changed through the years and the earliest examples were all metal, although the commonest found today have an enamel centre for the figures and a pressed brass surround. These are 19th century. It is remarkable that the type went on being made for so long, for production did not end till 1914. The movements were durable and comparatively trouble free, and these clocks are now enjoying great popularity with collectors in all countries.

The earliest of the type had verge escapements with teeth of the scapewheel pointing downwards. The pallets were long, to keep down the amplitude, and the pendulum was made in sections to provide easy transport. A peculiarity of the movement was that it struck the hour again two minutes after having first done so. This was to enable the strokes to be counted if they had previously been missed. The striking mechanism presents some unusual features such as a rack that descends vertically just as striking is about to begin without 'warning'. On later clocks pendulums were placed at the front of the movement instead of at the rear, and some of them were very largely made out of sheet brass pressed into all kinds of designs and coloured. The type is sufficiently popular for reproductions to be made with the traditional type of movement, although these have an anchor escapement instead of the verge.

A further development of the Comtoise movement was spring driven and contained in a case having an irregular shape with a dial of about 20cm diameter — much smaller than the dial plate proper. These clocks were meant to hang on the wall and have been christened 'Vineyard' clocks in recent years, and have also been made with movements approximating to the typical French spring driven movement. Some of the German factories also produced this type and it is difficult to distinguish between the French and German examples.

The lantern clock has also been produced in France but the proportions are different from the English type and sometimes a very ornate dial with the figures on separate enamel plaques can be seen. The movements are, however, further derivatives of the Gothic wall clock design.

The French clock in the 18th century was considered a piece of furniture with a functional mechanism attached, and the importance was not in the movement but how the piece blended with the other furnishings of the room. Dials tend to be small in comparison with the total size of the case, and the movement only occupies a small amount of the total volume.

Factory made movements were often imported into Britain without cases which were made locally. In the late 19th century black marble was very popular and a design based on a Greek temple is often seen. Plain cases were also popular, and while the black marble style is not now liked, there is a great advantage in that the weight of the clock prevents its being shifted for dusting. Regulation is performed by means of a key operating on a little square over the figure 12. Many French movements had pin pallet escapements placed before the dial and the action can be seen clearly. The better quality clocks have agate pallets instead of steel. Whatever the escapement, a French clock of the traditional type usually gives excellent results.

However, there are cheaper types of French movement and these are usually provided with tiny pendulums and 'Tictac' escapements. This escapement receives impulse on every other beat, and after the spring has run down to a certain extent the friction is enough to stop the clock. F.J. Britten condemned the type in his *Watch and Clockmaker's Handbook* and many of the clocks have had platform escapements with balances fitted to replace the original. If one is collecting and not buying a clock for telling the time, the tictac version is naturally preferable. These movements were usually supplied in a brass drum that allowed virtually any type of case to be fitted.

A now very popular French speciality is the 'Pendule de Voyage' or Carriage Clock. There are also English examples of these, but they usually have fusees, while the French models do not. French makers seem to have abandoned the fusee as soon as the pendulum was applied, following the precedent set by the earliest Haagse Klokjes made by Coster. Carriage clocks were generally produced in the rough at St Nicholas d'Aliermont, near Dieppe, and sent to Paris to be finished where numerous workshops would each do the work according to the ideas of the proprietor. Platform escapements were made in the French watchmaking area round Besançon, and no doubt some of the clocks were also finished there. The movements of carriage clocks are very similar in style and finish to those of pendulum clocks.

GERMANY

The Gothic wall clock was an important type in Germany in the 15th century, but with the coming of the Renaissance production was concentrated on spring clocks of high quality, the two most important centres for makers being Augsburg and Nuremberg. Augsburg gained a reputation for automata clocks and these could consist of animals that moved their eyes, cows that could be milked after the owner had filled a special container with milk, and other moving figures and processions. Both towns produced table clocks with astronomical indications. Other German cities also had their craftsmen and one sees clocks that have originated in such places as Munich, Prague and Ulm, to mention but three. The table clock went on being produced longer in Germany than elsewhere and examples are known from the late 17th century to the early 18th. Because of the control by guilds, which would not allow standards to be reduced, the South German cities lost their hold upon the market, and long case and bracket clocks were made elsewhere which, although not exactly similar to British examples, certainly owed something to them. Particular mention should be made of Leopold Hoyss of Bamberg, who made some elaborate bracket clocks bearing a resemblance to the English models, but which were carried on curved feet and incorporated curves in the outline of the case whereas the British clocks would be formed with straight lines.

The long case clock was also made in Germany, especially in Northern towns, and although the movements bore some resemblance to those of British, the cases were straighter and the division between hood, trunk and base less pronounced.

The type of German clock that was best known outside Germany was the Black Forest clock. The peasants in the Black Forest were prevented from doing farm work in the winter on account of the severe weather and many of them took to woodcarving as an occupation for the winter months. Legend has it that a wooden wheeled clock was brought from Bohemia and some Black Forest woodcarvers imitated it, producing clocks for their own use. Later, more clocks were produced so they could be sold, with some of the men deciding to give up farming and concentrate on full-time clockmaking. This was in the early 18th century and by the middle of that century the trade was well established. The son of one of the men had been to Paris to find out what types of tools could be made; and after that the Black Forest developed a style of clock that was all its own. At first very little metal was used but in about 1780 brass casting was introduced into the area and wheels were then made of brass, although the frames and arbors of the clocks still continued to be made of wood. The pendulum was late in being introduced, clocks still being made with the foliot as late as 1750, but the design had settled down by about 1800, to a white painted arch dial with two brass hands, exposed weights and pendulum hanging beneath it. When the pendulum was first introduced it was very short and swung in front of the dial. As the clockmakers were familiar with farming this short pendulum was christened a 'Cow Tail'. In the early 19th century the Black Forest clock was being exported all over Europe, mostly sold by itinerant members of the community who had established themselves in some town with a stock of clocks and then went out every day until they were sold. Sometimes they would return home after this but more often they arranged for a regular supply to be sent to their depot. Some of the members of the group would be away from home for several years.

Some of the Black Forest clocks were quite complicated in spite of having movements made mostly of wood, and even included quarter chimes or music, often played on glass bells. Clocks made for the British market nearly always have circular dials surrounded by a mahogany rim and covered by a convex glass. After 1842 American competition gradually took over the Black Forest market and changes were made in the design of the cases while still retaining the old type of movement. Some clocks were made like a picture frame with a circular dial smaller than the original type. The rest of the space in the frame would be occupied by a painting; sometimes this featured an animal or human figure which moved its eyes in time with the pendulum. Another way of decorating the frame was to fill it with a design in pressed brass similar to the dial surrounds of the Comtoise clocks.

The so called 'Biedermeier' style came in about 1860. The movement was enclosed in a small cabinet type of case, often with pillars and entablature, vaguely suggesting the French clocks of the Empire period. The pillars were sometimes of white alabaster.

In spite of all improvements, the original type of Black Forest clock was doomed, and the only way for the producers to survive was to change over to producing American type clocks in factories instead of in small workshops as had been the case with the traditional Black Forest type. The latter did hold on for somewhat longer, made without striking but with alarm work only, generally known as 'Postman's Alarms'. The first clocks on the American principle were very close copies of those from across the Atlantic, but the papers in the back do not usually state the maker's name. As much as possible was done to suggest that the clocks were, in fact, of American manufacture, but generally speaking the Black Forest article was of slightly better quality, thicker sheets of metal being used for the plate of the movement and the dial. The cases, however, were generally rather rough and finished by applying stain and polish to the wood of the case itself, while the American cases were usually veneered. It is quite common to find the inside of the case of a Black Forest clock of this period painted blue.

Clocks made on the American plan included timepieces, alarms and clocks with striking, but quite soon German designs began to appear which involved decoration of the cases by carving and turning. American clocks often had painting on the glass door to hide the pendulum, with the top portion of the door left blank to render the dial and hands visible, and a German variation of this idea was to let the whole of the door be covered by painting, leaving a circular opening where the dial came. This was an echo of the idea of the clocks with paintings in a frame previously mentioned.

A popular type with the German factories was the so-called 'Regulator', a wall clock often with an American type movement and less often with a movement of better quality. The case had glass on three sides and was generally based on the Vienna Regulator, but the majority of the German products were spring driven. The pendulum was of the gridiron type suggesting that it was compensated for temperature, but this was not always the case; the idea being generally to promote sales while the compensation was artificial. The bob of the pendulum usually bore the letters 'R/A' (Retard/Avance). The clocks were produced generally in three sizes, the usual size used for a Vienna regulator but with spring drive, a size with a total length of about 1m and a miniature size. The intermediate size is by far the most popular. The German factories also produced the Vienna Regulator with its brass weights and dead beat escapement but the finish was not nearly so good as that of the originals produced in Vienna itself. A firm in Austria that produced Vienna Regulators under factory conditions was taken over by the German firm of Junghans in 1901.

The factories in the Black Forest were able to greatly increase their trade, especially with Britain which was far and away the best customer. Later developments included wall clocks in oak cases with bevelled glasses and wooden rods to the pendulums. These clocks first appeared about 1912 and were very popular in the 1920s. During the latter years Germany also produced many mantel clocks of the 'Napoleon's hat' type and a variety of smaller clocks controlled by balances which bear some affinity to the usual type of alarm clock. Many of these had movements about 2in in diameter and were known in the trade as 'Two inch' clocks.

Clockmaking had also been established in Silesia by a man called Gustav Becker, to whom the Prussian Government had given a subsidy. Other firms followed his example and after Becker's death all the factories were amalgamated. Production was much on the lines of the Black Forest factories, and many clocks were exported to Britain and other countries. Becker's speciality was a German version of the Vienna Regulator; but many other styles featured in the catalogues.

The cuckoo clock had been invented in the Black Forest about 1730 and was first produced in the style of the normal Black Forest clock, but about 1870 the well known design with carved leaves was introduced, and is still being made today. Smaller versions are also made, some being spring driven with china dials and others in the shape of a Black Forest house.

Many German firms are now going in for reproductions, the spring driven regulator being a popular model. Other firms are producing versions of the oldest form of Black Forest clock in wood with a foliot controller. Many of these clocks can be purchased in kit form for self construction. The traditional wall clock with the painted arch dial is also being produced, but modern versions are not made to resemble the old models very closely. The dials are flat instead of having a convex portion where the figures come, and the movements are usually eight day which involves heavier and larger weights which look wrong. In addition the weights are in brass cases which were only seen in the very late clocks of the picture frame or Biedermeier type.

AUSTRIA

Clockmaking in Austria followed much the same pattern as in Germany until the late 18th century. Possibly it was the marriage of Marie Antoinette with Louis XVI that provided the affinity between Austrian and French styles. In any case, we find that the Austrians were fond of small movements with delicately made parts and also the fashion for Arabic figures, that began in Paris, was perpetuated in Vienna. The Austrian clock best known outside its own country is the Vienna Regulator. These were made as precision timekeepers and the cases were glazed on three sides so that the pendulum, weights and movement could be inspected. The earliest examples had a distinct trunk, hook and base like an English long case clock, but later examples had a longer case all in one piece. The glass sides gave the type the name of 'Laterndluhr' (Lantern clock) which should not be confused with the English clocks bearing that name. Some of the early Vienna Regulators had various complications such as day of the month, day of the week, moonphase, etc, and even these clocks were made quite small. The weight drive, wooden pendulum rods, which do not expand or contract very much with changes in temperature, and the dead beat escapements gave these clocks a very high standard of performance.

The earliest Vienna Regulators had plain dials and were hand-made, but by the mid-19th century the dials were acquiring the distinctive brass ring inside the figures and attempts were made to produce the clocks by factory methods. This was not entirely successful. The firm of Gebrüder Resch of Ebensee produced these clocks in a factory but were taken over by the German firm of Junghans in 1901. An Austrian clock usually has the gong attached to the movement while the German version has it attached to the case.

Another type of clock associated with Vienna was the picture frame clock, but, unlike the later examples made in the Black Forest, the picture was generally replaced by a matted or decorated background. Many of these clocks chimed the quarters on the Austrian system and, unlike the Black Forest version, they were spring driven. The movements resembled French work, but many Austrian spring clocks only run for two or three days on a winding.

The Austrian system of sounding the quarters is to give one blow on a bell for each quarter, i.e. one at quarter past, two at half past, etc, and then sound the number of the hour on a different toned bell after the four quarters have been sounded. Many of the turret clocks in Austria have the figures I to IIII inside the hour figures and the hand that points to them, which virtually performs the function of a minute hand, is shorter than the hour hand. This idea was used on early domestic clocks, but the normal arrangement of hands is found on productions of the late 18th century and after.

Many Austrian mantel clocks are built with the dial above supported by white pillars, giving the appearance of a small pavilion. These often have the quarter striking.

The country districts used the 'Brettluhr' or 'Board clock', which was a simple movement placed at the top of a vertical board which was hung on the wall. The clock was weight driven and had a long pendulum. A further Austrian type was the 'Zappler' (Wriggler) which was a tiny spring clock perhaps 50mm high with a pendulum working in front of the dial. These clocks had a version of the tictac escapement mentioned in the section on France.

Austrian mantel clocks are also found in bronze cases which resemble French products and use is made of statuettes in the design. Later Austrian products are in very heavy and overpowering wooden cases which typify the late 19th century for most countries, including the USA.

ITALY

Some authorities claim that Italy was one of the nations which contributed to the invention of the clock. Certainly early written records from Italy mention clocks and many of the Italian cities possessed public clocks at an early date. The Tarsia panels seen in museums often show these clocks and it seems that it was popular in Italy to have the dial revolve and the time indicated by a stationary hand. These clocks include both the monastic alarm type and the turret clock.

As far as domestic clocks were concerned, Italy seems to have made the table variety, and there is one of these in the Science Museum in London; dated 1656; it has been claimed to be the oldest pendulum clock in existence, but it cannot be stated that this evidence is trustworthy.

The German monk, Paulus Almanus, describes a number of clocks seen in Rome during his stay there in the 1470s, but it is not known whether all these were of Italian make or obtained from elsewhere. Italy had its own version of the English lantern clock, and these are found with normal dials, rotating dials and dials with only six hours instead of twelve, which facilitates telling the time with one hand provided one knows which quarter of the day one is in.

A speciality of the 17th century was the night clock which was able to show the time by means of a lamp shining through holes cut in the shape of Roman figures. These clocks were contained in ebonised cases which were shaped like altars and therefore cause the clocks to be called 'Altar Clocks'.

MALTA

The island of Malta produced its own type of clock in the early 19th century. These resembled large picture frames and were decorated with gesso and gilding, usually having 'ear' pieces at the top. The movements were small and driven by weights whose cords were carried upwards and over pulleys to give the weight the maximum amount of fall, and still keep it entirely within the case. American shelf clocks had the same system. The dial occupied the upper part of the case and below was a slot to allow the pendulum bob to be seen and show at a glance if the clock was still going. These very colourful clocks did not often leave the island and are therefore rare. Some people have replaced the movements with electric ones, but a clock of the original type is very interesting to possess even if it only runs for fifteen hours on a winding.

SWITZERLAND

The Swiss clockmaking of the early days is best summed up by the work of the Liechti family in Winterthur. At the beginning of the 16th century they were producing turret clocks and, for many generations, they produced Gothic wall clocks, many of which are to be seen in the museum at Winterthur and in other European museums. The country places did not lag behind the towns and clocks with wooden wheels were produced that show a high standard of workmanship. Some were even arranged for the clock to repeat while using the count wheel form of striking.

Switzerland's horological fame rests rather on watches than on clocks, the watchmaking area being in the west of the country in the Jura. Clocks were also produced here. Beginning with a simple black cased wall clock that was weight driven, the story of the Haagse Klokje being developed by French makers virtually repeats itself.

The spring driven clocks made in the 18th century and later can be traced as evolving from the simple wall clock previously mentioned, and the Swiss models bear a general resemblance to those from mid-18th century France, except that gilding was less popular and the cases were finished either in colour or the natural finish of the wood. Swiss clocks possessed the enamel dials found on those from France, and the pendulums were also to be seen swinging behind the glass. The clocks are known as the 'Neuchâtel' style and are still being made as reproductions, usually with a bracket to match which is not always a feature of the French clocks. The long case clock has not been extensively made in Switzerland.

The maximum variety in Swiss clocks can be found in the wall models from country districts which are derivatives of the Gothic wall clocks, but which sometimes contain plate movements. The Restaurant 'zur Kathrin' at Oerlikon displays a large number of these clocks. Some have pendulums in front of the dial, others have jacks for striking, but all illustrate the great variety in which the clocks were made. In the Kellenberger collection at Winterthur representative types from the various valleys can be seen. Very few of the Swiss clocks of the factory era were made as the country concentrated on the production of watches.

SPAIN

Spanish clocks are not often seen. It is believed that the country imported its requirements mostly from France. Some clocks of the lantern type are known, however.

SCANDINAVIA

Literature on Scandinavian clockmaking is not profuse. The National Museum at Copenhagen and the 'Old Town' at Aarhus show that some interesting clocks were being made in Denmark both in the Renaissance period and in the 18th century, and many old turret clocks are to be found in the country. Perhaps the best known type of Danish clock is the 'Bornholm'. The story goes that a cargo of English clocks on its way to Russia was wrecked on the island of Bornholm and, having been salvaged by the inhabitants, were copied by them. Later, production grew to such an extent that the clockmakers in Copenhagen were complaining about the competition.

The Bornholm clock is not unlike the English model, but both case and movement are country work. The cases are often painted white or various colours, and sometimes the mouldings are decorated with gilt. The legend of the wrecked cargo dates from the mid-18th century, so Bornholm clocks should not be found resembling English clocks of an earlier period.

Clockmaking in Sweden followed the general pattern of that in other European countries, but in the late 18th century the tendency developed to change to French styles. Arabic figures were fashionable and a type of long case clock, based on the French outline, was made; today this is known as the Farmhouse Clock. These are often painted in colours much lighter than would be associated with English clocks. The movements were of the plate type and one would expect to find wooden barrels.

UNITED STATES OF AMERICA

The story of the American clock is a fascinating one. It began with clockmakers from Britain making the types that they were used to, as well as further clocks of the newer types being imported, but after 1776 the pattern changed for two reasons. The first was the shortage of raw materials, and the second was the influx of settlers from all parts of Europe who brought their own ideas with them and modified the product which up till then had been purely British in style.

The first type of American clock was the 'Case on Case' type. This gave the impression of a mantel clock standing on a small cabinet, the length of the case allowing the weight to have sufficient fall, for the clock was still weight driven. Springs were expensive and had to be imported and the problem of making steel springs cheaply in America was not overcome until the late 1840s. Up to that time clocks of the highest quality were weight driven except for a very small number of bracket clocks in the English style. These are very rare.

The case on case type had movements smaller than the English eight day long case clocks, but the design was similar and the finish, too, was in the English style. Many were purely timepieces to save metal. Brass was so short that when movements were imported from Birmingham, the American clockmaker would cut off the corner of the plate and supply himself with a piece of brass for his workshop. Some British movements had the top right hand pillar set in which, from a technical point of view, is an improvement, but as few movements of this type are seen in Britain we infer that these models were produced specially for the American market.

In 1802 Simon Willard of Roxbury patented a new style of clock. It was a wall clock something less than 1m in height with the movement contained in a drum shaped portion of the case slightly wider than the dial. Below was a tapered section that contained the weight, and at the bottom was a rectangular portion with a door containing a glass tablet giving access to the pendulum bob for regulation. The movement was like the going side of an English long case clock made in miniature but had some important modifications. The pendulum hung at the front, between the movement and dial, and allowed the thickness of the case to be reduced. A loop had to be made to clear the tubes that carried the hands. The weight was made long and tapered and descended on the centre line of the clock just below the movement and behind the pendulum. The barrel, and hence the winding hole, was at figure 2 which gave a few centimetres more for the weight to fall through. The pendulum was protected from the weight by a thin partition at the bottom of the case to prevent interference should the weight start to swing. The main wheel was made very large and the barrel comparatively small to help to give as long a running time as possible, and this meant that the weight had to be heavy.

This type of clock is now known as a 'Banjo' and is very highly prized by American collectors. It is extremely rare in Britain, but there is a firm in London that makes reproductions. Replicas of the Banjo and the Case on Case have also been made in the USA in recent years, as well as the development of the Banjo called the 'Girandole', which has a large circular base instead of the rectangular one and features more decoration on the case.

The cheaper end of the market was supplied by movements roughly corresponding to the English eight day long case type but made of wood and running only for thirty hours. Eli Terry of Plymouth Conn., had the idea of producing these clocks in large numbers and signed a contract with two brothers who were to market them. Terry took a year to build a factory which was powered by a water wheel and there made large numbers of parts which were subsequently assembled. This laid the foundation for today's mass production methods. Everyone thought that Terry was mad, but he completed his contract for 4,000 clocks and after that sold his factory to his two assistants, Thomas and Hoadley.

He had further plans for making clocks. The type that he had so far produced could be hung on the wall just as it came, or put into a long case according to the financial means of the purchaser. Terry now planned to make a clock that incorporated a similar type of movement to the previous model but which could have its weights entirely enclosed within the case and, therefore, was capable of standing on a shelf instead of hanging. The idea involved selling the movement and the case together so the clock left the factory ready for use. He built a new factory and after a few years evolved his first model. This was contained in a rectangular case and had a door at the front, with a glass that allowed the movement and pendulum to be seen. There was no dial, the figures being painted in reverse on the back of the glass. The weights hung from cords which were carried over pulleys at the top of the case and therefore descended beside, and not directly below, the movement.

After a short period of producing this model, later Terry movements were put into pillar and scroll cases, which remained popular for some years until ousted by a taller case which cost less to make and yet sold for a higher price. Terry was interested in improving his first idea and evolved several movements to fit the pillar and scroll case.

As Terry was financially successful, many others imitated him and a large horological industry grew up in Connecticut. The factory clock took over from the English type of long case which was still being imported and also made in America. This type, known as a 'Tall' clock in USA, had probably almost died out by 1830, while in Britain it lasted a good forty years more.

In 1837 there was a financial panic in USA and many manufacturers were ruined. One of the factory owners, Chauncey Jerome, who at one time made cases for Terry, had the idea of a cheap brass movement clock to replace the cheap wooden one. Rolled brass was being produced in Connecticut for other industries and there was a ready source of raw material. Jerome's brother designed a simple movement and rectangular cases were designed which had an ogive moulding at the front and were therefore known as 'OGs'. The OG is the most important of all American designs. They were turned out in their thousands, not only by Jerome who began exporting in 1842, but by other makers also. The wooden clocks had not formed an export commodity but the flood of brass clocks going from America to Europe killed the Black Forest industry, and Black Forest makers were forced themselves to produce clocks in factories to the American pattern.

The OGs were, of course, weight driven, for as yet the making of steel

44

mainsprings had not been accomplished on a commercial scale in the USA. Some makers overcame this by fitting the OG movement into a smaller case and providing the motive power by leaf springs, which were anchored in the bottom of the case and bent as the clock was wound. Other makers did the same thing but put, as a motive power unit, some stiff steel springs in the bottom and wooden fusees on the same arbor. Some makers used springs of brass but these became fatigued in time. Luckily the spring problem was solved in the late 1840s and then a large number of striking clocks, alarm clocks and timepieces were manufactured. The wooden movement had virtually ceased to be made by about 1844.

American clocks were exported to all parts of the world and are therefore known to a large number of collectors. As the 19th century wore on, new models were introduced, such as the 12in (30cm) wall dial with a trunk below having a window to show the pendulum bob. These are known as 'Schoolhouse' clocks in America.

In the last years of the 19th century cases were made with much more decoration and lost the simplicity which characterises the earlier factory products. Some cases were made of wood with a finish to imitate marble, as the French clocks with marble cases were very popular in Britain and other European countries. Some of these clocks were made with visible escapements as were the French models. An important modification to the movement was necessary for the 'marble' style, viz that the pendulum had to be removed from the front of the movement to the back. These clocks can usually be told at a glance from the French product; on the American clock the winding holes are on the chapter ring whereas on the French clock they are much closer to the centre of the dial.

The final type of American clock to be imported into Britain before 1914 was usually contained in a lancet type case; it had a dial with Arabic figures and no means of regulation except by a key working on a square at the figure 12.

While Connecticut styles accounted for most of the clock production in America, some products of higher quality were made. Seth Thomas produced a weight driven regulator which was sold from 1863 to 1950. Other manufacturers produced similar styles. The Howard Company of Boston produced the banjo clock in a less decorative and more utilitarian style. Many factories had their own versions of the calendar clock to show the day of the month and the week, and Welch Spring & Company produced a number of clocks that were intended to be of a higher quality than the usual factory product.

The lot of the collector of American clocks is made easier by the fact that many of the old manufacturers' catalogues are being reprinted and provide a wonderful aid in identifying items that turn up.

Seth Thomas and Ansonia both produced movements with circular plates to resemble the French type, and a popular line of clocks of higher quality in the early years of this century was the 'Crystal Regulator'. In Britain these clocks are generally of French manufacture and are known as 'Four Glass'.

After the Black Forest factories had gone over to the American type movement they produced a number of clocks which are unmarked, and it is an interesting exercise to decide the country of origin when a nameless clock appears. Types so far seen which could belong to either country are small timepieces with a pendulum, Sharp Gothic alarm and Striking clocks, eight day drop dials, and a balance controlled clock in an octagonal wooden case known in America as 'Marine or Locomotive'. Two OGs by Junghans have also been noted, but while the type appeared in American catalogues until 1914, it was not made in Germany for very long.

JAPAN

Before Japan introduced the Western style of timekeeping in 1873, Japanese clocks operated on a highly complicated system. Day and night were each divided into six periods, each period averaging two hours by our system but becoming shorter or longer as the seasons changed.

It is believed that the Dutch introduced mechanical clocks into Japan, and that these were of the Gothic type with the foliot. With the changing length of the Japanese hours it was necessary to change the position of the weights night and morning. Later the clock was designed to operate with two foliots, and it automatically changed from one to the other as day gave way to night, and vice versa. Adjustment of the weights was still necessary but did not need to be done so frequently, probably by a clockmaker once a fortnight. The hours were numbered 9,8,7,6,5,4, and the striking of the clock was so arranged that one blow was sounded half way through the hours following an odd number of blows on the bell and two strokes following the even numbers. The progression then became 9,1,8,2,7,1,6,2,5,1,4,2.

A later type of clock was controlled by a balance and balance spring, but this type ran at a constant speed and the variation in length of the hours had to be allowed for by having a rotating dial with a fixed pointer and the hour numbers on adjustable plaques which could be moved closer to or away from each other.

The third main type of Japanese clock used the driving weight as an indicator and a new scale was supplied for it to travel along each month. Some clocks were made with a comprehensive scale which was intended to be read at a different point according to the time of the year. Movable plaques have also been associated with this type.

After 1873 Japan adopted the European system of time measurement and clocks were factory made, usually on the American principle. Large numbers of these clocks, particularly of the Schoolhouse type, are now being imported into the USA for American collectors. So far no Japanese copy of an early American model has been seen, but some clocks of the style of the turn of the century have been noted with a letter S in a diamond as a trade mark, which at a distance resembles the mark of Seth Thomas. One Schoolhouse clock has been seen with a paper inside marked 'Ansonia Type' as a possible incentive to would-be buyers, as the Schoolhouse type was a speciality of the Ansonia Co of New York.

We therefore have a new type of clock for collectors, a Japanese imitation of American models, in the same way that we have the Black Forest imitations of them.

English Birdcage Type movement.
This was the English development of
the Gothic movement and was used
for lantern clocks and thirty hour long
case clocks.

The same movement from the rear
showing the Count Wheel which controls
the number of blows struck.

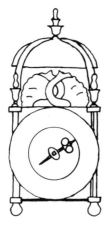

The English lantern clock. This example
is of the middle period. Earlier clocks
had a much narrower chapter ring, and
on later clocks the dial was much wider.

48

A lantern type movement in a hooded case. This early 18th-century clock has a single hand and alarm.

A lantern clock of the early 18th century. The dial has become very much wider than the case and approximates to that of a long case clock.

A pair of long case clocks about 1700.
The marquetry belongs to the late 17th
century and the walnut to the early 18th.

Dial of clock by Jonas Barber, Ratcliff Cross c1690. Note spandrels with single cherub's head and the quarter and half hour marks. The contrast between the slender minute hand and broad hour hand is very marked.

Long case clock by Richard Hardwick of Ashwick. This shows later 18th-century development. The arch dial carries a moonphase and high water indicator, the quarter hour marks have disappeared, and the minute figures are nearly as large as the hour figures. The fluted columns on the hood indicate the Classical Revival. The hands are later.

Single handed dial of thirty hour clock by Thos Shinn, Mathan mid-18th Century. These clocks are difficult to date precisely as they kept repeating older features. This type of dial is often associated with an eight day movement, but the substitution is given away by the absence of minute marks.

This clock is typical of the end of the period in which long case clocks were made. Although London made, the type was then not fashionable in London and was probably an order from the country. Clocks of this type with circular dials are often seen with Scottish makers' names on them.

This long case clock dates from the beginning of the 19th century. Arabic figures were popular about 1800-20. The case is more ornate than the usual British clock at this period and suggests the type of case that was then being produced in America.

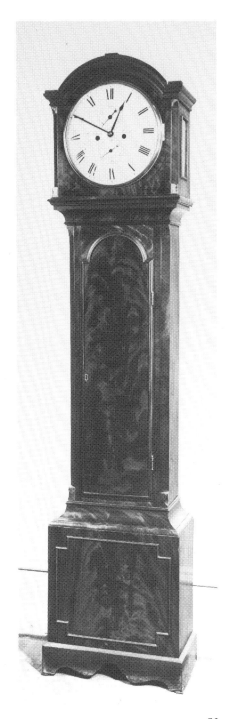

This dial from a thirty hour long case clock dates from about 1800. The dots to indicate minutes and the large minute figures and the circles inside and outside the figures, suggesting the old separate chapter ring of the brass dial clocks, are typical of this period. The disc for showing the days of the month often bears the name of the dialmaker.

This thirty hour dial is a little later. The minute figures have disappeared and the painting in the corners has a mechanical appearance. It was not common for thirty hour clocks to have seconds, and the fact that this clock has day of the month as well indicates that it was of a quality above that of the usual country clock of that time.

This is a very late clock dating from 1850-60. It is of good quality but very plain and the hands are of brass. Both the two latter clocks have their weights suspended from rope rather than chain.

By the late 17th century the spring
driven clock looked like this. Note
the domed top, single cherub's head
spandrels, quarter and half hour marks
and contrasting hands. Like many clocks
of this type, this one does not strike but
repeats hours and quarters when the cord
is pulled.

The bracket clock has grown taller and now has an arch dial. Half and quarter hour marks are present and, in addition, those for the half-quarters. The day of the month indicator is in the arch. The slot between X and II contains a little indicator attached to the pendulum so it can be seen at a glance if the clock is still going. These clocks were intended to be moved about and might stop if placed too far out of the proper level. The handle at the top assists in carrying the clock.

This clock takes us later into the
18th century. The spandrels are less
characteristic, the quarter hour marks
have disappeared and the minute hand
has more decoration. This example
strikes every hour but can be silenced
by the dial in the arch.

These two clocks show the later development of the bracket clock. The carrying handles have disappeared and the cases are much plainer. The dials are plainer and circular. The finish is now mahogany with a little inlay.

The brass inlay that was popular in the early 19th century shows up to advantage in this clock. It was an echo of the applied metal decoration of the 18th century (see pages 56 and 57) and the carrying handles here are decorative rather than functional

Here is the inside of an early 19th-century bracket clock. The rear plate of the movement is engraved and also the pendulum bob. The brass support pieces for the movement are typical.

This clock is almost into the Victorian period. The dial is painted white instead of silvered and the hands are extremely plain. The case is beginning to show signs of over decoration.

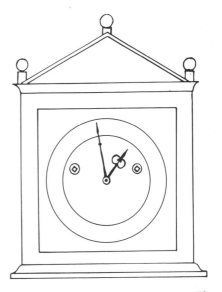

The earliest spring driven pendulum clocks made in England resembled this. The architectural case is contemporary with the similar cases used for long case clocks c1660-75, and the high winding holes indicate an early movement.

In the early 19th century there was a fashion for clock cases in the French style. This is a typical example and could easily pass for a French clock until the movement is examined.

The rear view of the clock shows the typically English arrangement of the movement occupying all the available space. The pendulum cock and the external pendulum are also very unlike French work.

In the 18th century it was necessary to
have clocks with prominent dials so that
travellers at inns could keep an eye on
the time, ready for coaches to depart.
These clocks were weight driven and had
a movement approximating to that of the
long case clock. This example is of late
18th century. Earlier ones had much
larger dials which were generally painted
black with gilt figures.

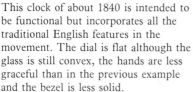

This clock of about 1840 is intended to be functional but incorporates all the traditional English features in the movement. The dial is flat although the glass is still convex, the hands are less graceful than in the previous example and the bezel is less solid.

In the late 18th century the standard English movement was adapted for use in wall clocks. By the early 19th century the cases were being made longer to take a longer pendulum and striking work was added. This is a tasteful example with mahogany case inlaid, and a convex dial and glass.

62

The later version of the Tavern clock often associated with Norwich. The dial is much smaller and striking work is present but the movement is still of the traditional English pattern.

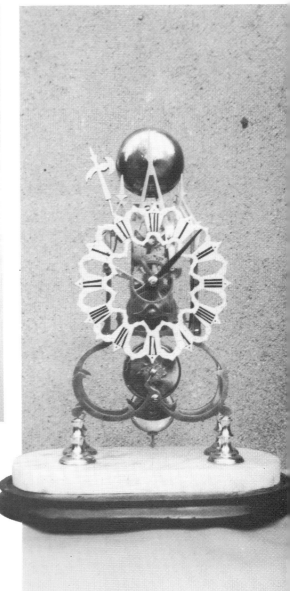

The Standard English movement was often provided with cutout plates and exhibited under a glass dome. The usual type was a timepiece as shown here. Cutting away the plates makes them theoretically weak and some very bad examples have been noted.

64

When a skeleton clock was provided with
striking work the appearance was very
confusing.

Here is a typical Zaanse Clock showing
the backboard which houses the
pendulum, the fret showing Faith, Hope
and Charity, and the two bells
surmounted by a figure of Atlas.

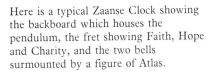

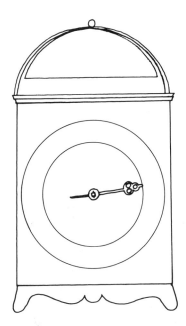

The Dutch version of the Gothic clock
in the early 17th century possessed less
height and was encased in sheet iron
plates decorated with paint. It led the
way to the Zaanse clock and the
Stoelklok.

The Stoelklok was mostly made in country places in the Netherlands and relied on cast lead frets and colour for its decoration. The movement was an adaption of the Gothic.

The Staartklok had the same movement as the Stoelklok except for the anchor escapement. It can be considered as the equivalent of the English thirty hour long case clock. The dial is in bright colours and there is plenty of polished brass to set it off. The three ornaments on the top of the hood are of thin pressed brass and are also decorated with colour.

One of the little clocks with a rapidly moving pendulum made for vessels plying the inland waterways of Holland. This Schippertje is conventional in having the six rayed star decoration in the bracket, but unusual in that it is not fitted with alarm work.

The Staartklok was sometimes made with a much shorter trunk and known as Kortkast.

67

A Dutch clock shop showing different varieties of stoel and staartklok.

View in another clock shop.

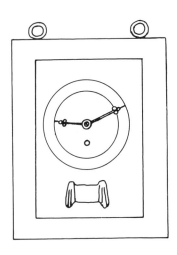

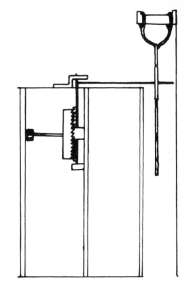

The first type of Haagse Kokje. Note the eyes for hanging the clock on the wall if desired.

The arrangement of the escapement in a stoelklok. The horizontal wire attached to the top of the verge works in a loop in the pendulum rod but, as their paths are different, the action is accompanied by a scraping noise.

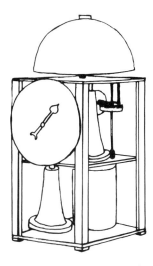

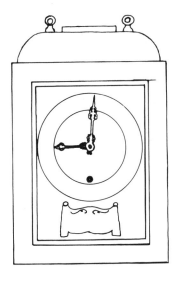

A Religieuse. This shows how the French makers were evolving their designs from the Haagse Klokje and gradually adding decoration. By the end of the reign of Louis XIV the clock had become much larger, very much more ornate and curves had taken the place of the straight lines of the Dutch model.

The arrangement of the trains of a table clock on two levels often used by French makers.

69

This clock of the Louis XV period shows how much the French makers had altered their clocks from the Dutch design. The height is increased, the pendulum is visible and the inside of the case is decorated. The outside of the case is ornamented with gilded bronze figures and the case and bracket are decorated with Buhl work, a marquetry made of sheets of tortoiseshell and brass. The figures are on separate enamel plaques and made at a time when it was not possible to produce a one piece dial of enamel.

The cartel clock was a popular French design that was also copied by other countries. This late 18th century example is not so highly decorated as the Louis XV clock and the dial is made in one piece. The hands are very elaborately decorated and are much better seen than on the previous clock. The case is gilt which remained popular in France for a very long time.

At the beginning of the 19th century clocks were popular which did not have gilt as the predominant motif in the decoration. Statuettes also became popular, especially Cupid and Venus. It is interesting to compare this case with that of the English clock in the similar style.

The Four Glass clock was a popular French design in the 19th century and was later imitated by American makers. This very fine clock has a dead beat escapement with agate pallets and is compensated on Ellicott's system. The date on the presentation plaque is 1868.

73

Here is a more decorated version of the
Four Glass. There are garlands of flowers
round the figures, a feature of the Louis
XVI period, and the hands are highly
decorated. The pendulum is compensated
by the mercury method, while the gong
indicates a date of middle to late 19th
century.

Clocks such as this were popular in
Victorian times. The gilded statuette and
the alabaster panels are met in a variety
of designs, and the dial and movement
are very typical mid-19th-century French
production, not only being seen in clocks
of this type, but also in black marble
cases of many designs.

In spite of having the name of a
Viennese maker on the dial this clock
can be considered a good example of
the Pendule d'Officier. The cord is for
making the clock repeat. The finish was
in the gilt so liked by French craftsmen.

The French lantern clock differed from the English type not only in decoration but in outline. The bottom of the fret follows the dial and the feet are longer.

The outline of a typical Capucine.

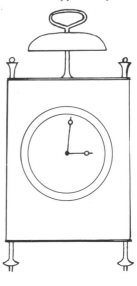

Here the gilded cupids are mounted on a case which shows more of the Victorian love of fussy detail. The quality of the case is not so good as the former but the movement is very similar. The clock would have been covered by a glass shade.

This clock is of much lower quality, the case being only of spelter which has been gilded, and the movement is a Tictac which was a poor timekeeper and prone to stop. The general ensemble when covered by a glass dome would deceive most visitors, and as many Victorian families never used their parlour but only kept it for show, there was nothing unusual in a clock that was not going.

The French equivalent of the English Dial was often housed in a case like this and the clocks are nowadays called Vineyard. The movements could be either spring driven versions of the Comtoise type or the usual French factory movement possessing either round or square plates. The door containing the glass opens upwards and can be awkward. Some German factories also produced this type.

Another Vineyard clock giving some indication of the variations in decoration that can be found. The figures 13 to 24 inside the normal hour figures were often found in France.

The movement of a Comtoise clock showing how it has developed from the Gothic type of movement, although the trains are placed side by side instead of one behind the other. The small scapewheel at the bottom is for working the alarm hammer. The linkage of the pendulum to the escapement can be seen on the right.

A typical Comtoise clock with decorated pendulum. The pendulum hangs at the front completely hiding the weights, and the circular enamel dial is surrounded by a pressed brass sheet. This clock is fairly late.

The Comtoise movement seen from the front. Note the bob weights at the right for making the striking levers descend smartly.

78

A Comtoise dial with a wheatsheaf motif.
The name of the vendor is on the dial
together with 'First quality guaranteed'.

The French also made skeleton clocks from the late 18th century onwards. This example has only three wheels in the train and all of them have wolf teeth.

The escapement is of the tictac type and the very light pendulum is supported by a silk thread. The base is of white alabaster.

A typical marble case that formed the housing of many thousands of French movements in the 19th century. This example is quite small and pleasing in appearance, but many are much too large and are not considered attractive by modern standards. Where the cases are large, the size of movement is not very much greater than on the small clocks.

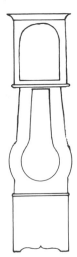

'Fiddle' type case often associated with Comtoise movements. The glass in the trunk allowed the elaborate pendulum to be seen.

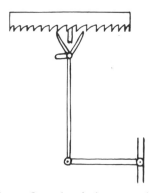

When a Comtoise clock possessed a verge escapement it was arranged upside down. The pallets were longer than usual to keep down the amplitude of the swing and the verge had to be cranked to avoid the scapewheel arbor which was supported by an adjustable bearing some way below the verge.

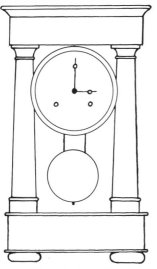

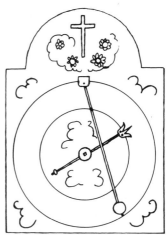

The type of French clock often known as Empire. The case could be of marble or wood and there were infinite ways of decorating it by inlay or applied ornaments. The pendulums were often of the gridiron type.

The country made German clock often had a small pendulum swinging before the dial. Outside the Black Forest area dials were often of sheet iron and decorated in colour. The movements were quite simple but still derived from the Gothic.

A feature of South German work was the Rack Clock where the movement itself is the driving weight and descends a toothed rack as it goes. Winding is effected by pushing the movement to the top again. Note the tiny pendulum in front of the dial. Many reproductions are now being sold.

Augsburg specialised in automata like this lion who rolls his eyes in time with the balance. The dial of the clock is placed on top.

The German long case clock was generally straighter than the British type but showed a certain amount of affinity with it. Some examples were very slender with the case made wider where the pendulum bob came.

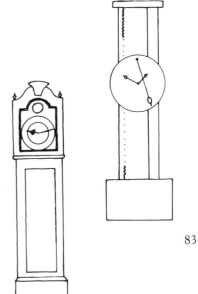

This Black Forest movement from
the early 19th century still possesses a
wooden frame but the wheels and arbors
are of metal. This one is even arranged
to sound the quarters. By this time the
Black Forest movement had reached a
standard of timekeeping greatly in excess
of what might have been expected.

84

This Black Forest movement is quite late but is arranged to run for eight days. It strikes on a wire gong instead of bells and incorporates a device allowing the hands to be turned backwards.

This Black Forest clock dates from the mid-18th century. All the wheels are of wood but striking is provided and incorporates a glass bell. The small pendulum swings before the dial which has been removed for photographic purposes. In spite of their roughness, these clocks functioned quite well.

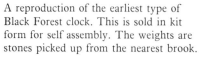

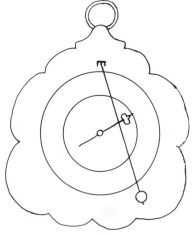

A reproduction of the earliest type of Black Forest clock. This is sold in kit form for self assembly. The weights are stones picked up from the nearest brook.

'Telleruhr' or Dish Clock with cowtail pendulum. Late 17th or early 18th century.

This is a typical Black Forest dial but is larger than usual, as it is intended for an eight day movement wound by a key. These movements occur sometimes in long cases of English make, but an English movement would have the winding holes much higher. The hands are a well known Black Forest design.

The circular dial with a plain wooden rim was extensively made in the Black Forest for the British market. These dials always had a brass bezel and convex glass but they are generally missing as in this example.

This Black Forest clock chimes the quarters by means of two jacks and a third one strikes the hours. Columns beside the chapter ring are a well-known feature of Black Forest dials.

This is a typical Black Forest clock with both strike and alarm made for the British market. In the early 19th century the clocks usually had striking only, and in the latter part of the century alarm only, when they were usually known as 'Postman's Alarms'.

The Biedermeier style often incorporated pillars in the design which could be of wood, alabaster or china. This is an ordinary striking wall clock of about 1860.

The cuckoo clock was a popular product of the Black Forest, but only in about 1870 did the case with carved leaves come into fashion. This case is in the Biedermeier style and dates from about 1860.

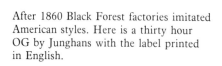

After 1860 Black Forest factories imitated American styles. Here is a thirty hour OG by Junghans with the label printed in English.

This striking mantel clock by Junghans c1880 could well be mistaken for an American product.

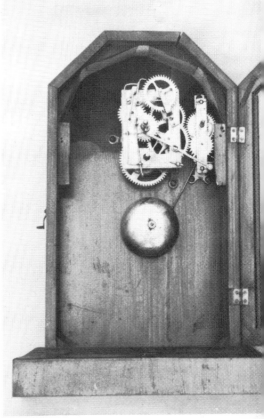

Here the separate alarm movement can be seen clearly.

American factories often produced a model that could be easily sold as a timepiece or an alarm. Here is the same idea on a German clock. The alarm work is separate from the main movement and can be added to as many clocks in the batch as desired. The pendulum is made to suggest mercury compensation but is of no value.

89

Two movements of the American type produced in Germany. The one on the left is very primitive and shows a certain amount of hand finishing, but the one on the right is much more sophisticated. Both would be c1870-80.

Two movements in varying cases. Both have the large scapewheel suggesting German work but the right hand example shows the German speciality of mounting a small movement in a large case.

This striking clock by Junghans c1890 shows a number of contemporary features. Carved finials, applied metal decoration to the case, dummy mercury pendulum and splayed base.

This timepiece has a painting on the glass door, the surrounds of the dial are also painted. This feature is rarely found on American clocks.

The popularity of the French marble clock led both German and American producers to imitate it. This clock has a wooden case that looks like marble at a distance. The movement is similar to the one on the right at the top of page 90, quite unlike the type that would have been fitted in a French clock.

This imitation marble clock does not deceive so well. The small finials at the side suggest wood rather than marble. This model has been seen with both timepiece and alarm movements.

A comparatively late alarm clock by H.A.C. The design is based on the traditional American one, but the glass is plain except for a small amount of painting. Decoration has been applied to the case itself while the base consists of the wood of the case being stained and polished. An American case would probably have been veneered.

Miniature novelty wall clock. The weights and chains are dummies and the clock is actually spring driven, the movement being an adaptation of the 2in balance movement.

92

This clock in the Biedermeier style is a transition between the traditional and American methods of production in the Black Forest. The movement is spring driven with all metal wheels, c1870.

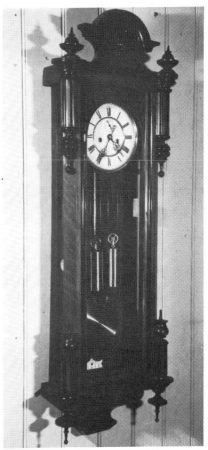

The Vienna Regulator as produced by a German factory. This is a high quality product but quality can vary from factory to factory.

A spring driven Regulator. This is the smallest model but still has the R/A pendulum with mock gridiron compensation.

By the 1920s this type had taken over from the R/A type of wall clock, often being fitted with quarter chimes, as in this example.

About the turn of the century German factories were producing mantel clocks like this. The movements and cases were solid but decorated with finials, pillars and applied ornaments.

Some German factories produced chiming clocks of very high quality such as this one by Lenzkirch. Large numbers were exported to Britain.

This model, known as a Freeswinger, or sometimes a Berliner, is not well known in Britain. It seems to have been a speciality for the home market in Germany.

The French clock also had its imitators which possessed a movement of similar type as well as the case. This little clock by Lenzkirch could easily be taken for French except that the hands are not typically of French design.

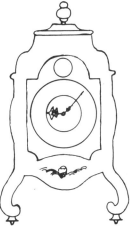

The type of Bracket Clock made by Leopold Hoyss.

The Laterndluhr, the precursor of the Vienna Regulator.

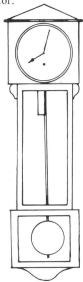

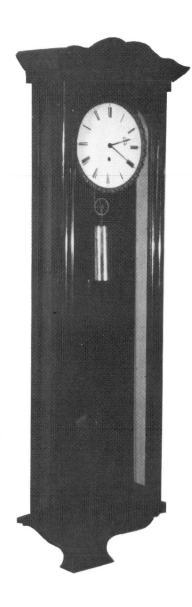

Austrian mantel clock with alabaster
pillars. The movement is fitted with
quarter chimes but the clock needs
winding about every two days.

A true Vienna Regulator — slim case,
one piece dial with a decorated surround,
slender hands and no unnecessary
decoration.

96

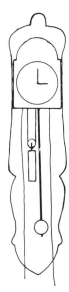

A Brettluhr (Plank clock). This is a movement mounted on a backboard that gives the clock its name. It can be considered the equivalent of the Dutch Staartklok or English thirty hour clock.

A Zappler (Wriggler). These clocks were so tiny and their pendulums so short that they moved at a high speed. They are more valued as a novelty than for their timekeeping capabilities.

The Italian version of the Lantern clock. This one has a six hour dial which helps the time to be read more exactly with only one hand. Other clocks had normal twelve hour dials with one or two hands, and sometimes rotating dials were fitted.

A Night Clock. The hour figure passes round the semi-circle indicating the quarters and is illuminated by a lamp inside the clock which shines through it. The figures are automatically changed each hour.

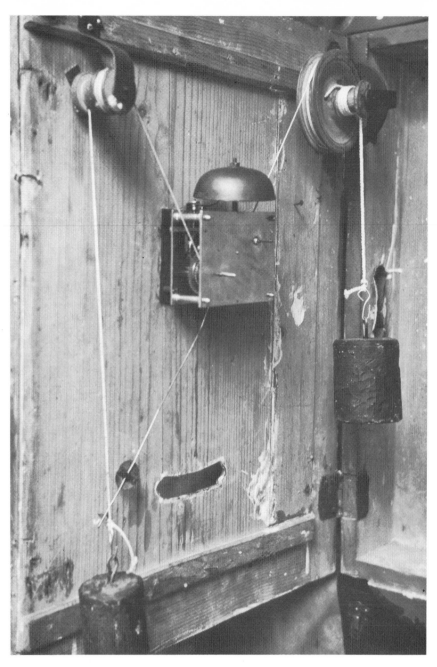

The movement of a Maltese clock. This one is provided with going and alarm and the double pulley on the going side increases the time of running but requires a heavier weight.

The dial of the Maltese clock. The slot below allows the pendulum to be seen and indicates whether the clock is still going. The case is finished in green with gilt decorations.

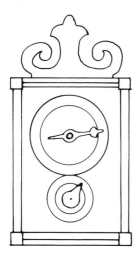

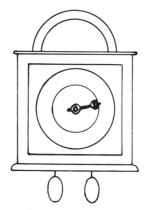

Early wall clock, metal dial, black case.

Wooden wheeled clock with separate quarter hour dial. The clock is controlled by a wheel balance. The dial is covered with paper which has been painted. Made in Davos c1670.

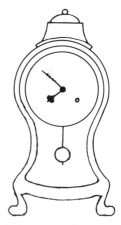

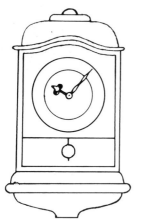

This clock shows a similar development to that which took place in France except that the applied metal ornaments are missing.

The previous design has now developed into a spring clock but still retains its original colouring. It approximates to the French Religieuse.

The style is now that known as Neuchâtel and the glass over the dial is domed. This type is very popular as a reproduction today.

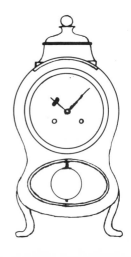

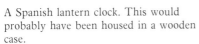

A Spanish lantern clock. This would probably have been housed in a wooden case.

The movement of the Spanish clock. In spite of being primitive it possesses mechanism for sounding hours and quarters.

The movement of a Scandinavian clock.
It owes a lot to the English eight day
long case clock but the plates are of iron.

Rear view of the Scandinavian movement
showing the Count wheel.

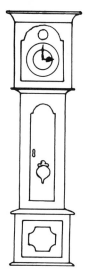

A typical case for a Bornholm clock. It approximate to English styles but tends to have more applied decoration as well as being painted in light colours.

A Swedish Farmhouse clock. The case suggests French long cases of the 18th century.

A Case on Case clock. Late 18th century. The kidney shaped opening for the dial was popular with this design. The winding hole is at 2 to give extra fall for the weight.

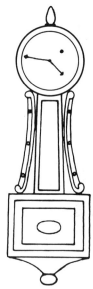

The Banjo clock. The weight is made long and tapered to fit the central portion of the case. The pendulum bob comes in the rectangular portion at the bottom. The curved arms at the sides are of brass. The base and central portion have glass panels with painting on them.

A modern reproduction of a Girandole. The design owes a lot to the Banjo clock but is more elaborately decorated.

An early wooden wheeled movement from Connecticut. In spite of having barrels the clock is wound by pulling up the cords.

Front view of the wooden movement.
The teeth of the wheels between the
plates lean forward to reduce friction.
The teeth of the dial wheels are straight.

Movement from the 9 o'clock side
showing the pins for lifting the hammer.

Rear view showing the Count Wheel.
Although this is not normally seen it is
decorated with turning. Observe how the
plates are fastened to the Seat Board.

The movement taken to pieces.

The Pillar and Scroll design c1820. The hands are of the same length but differ in design.

The Pillar and Scroll case with the movement in position. The back plate rests against the back of the case as the pendulum and Count Wheel have been brought to the front.

A typical OG. This has the convex moulding on the outer edge and the concave moulding on the door making it an OOG.

A variation of the OG case that used the same movement but got its inspiration from the later wooden wheeled shelf clocks of the 1830s.

A later OG. This clock has the door decorated with a transfer and the hands are of the spade pattern. The mouldings are flat. New Haven Clock Co, late 19th century.

An OG case open showing the typical
movement and the paper which carries a
picture of the factory and instructions for
setting the clock running and keeping it
in order. The paper is an important
feature for a collector but not many are
as well preserved as this one.

The idea of fitting a separate mechanism for alarm goes back to the days of the wooden wheeled shelf clock. Here it is incorporated in an OG by E.N. Welch who was one of the largest producers of clocks in Connecticut.

The arrangement of mainspring and fusee together. The fusee is a cone and not of the usual waisted shape employed when barrel and fusee are separate.

An early attempt at spring drive by an American factory. The movement is a normal eight day OG such as was fitted to weight driven clocks and the springs are mounted below with fusees on the same arbors. This clock dates from the late 1840s.

A simple label fitted into a timepiece. Such labels as this which do not mention the manufacturer's name can cause confusion as to whether the clock is of German or American origin.

A Sharp Gothic clock by Brewster and Ingrahams. 1844-52. This design of case was introduced by Elias Ingraham and remained popular for many years. The lock on the door with a separate key indicates an early production.

This case was also introduced by Elias Ingraham and was known as Round Gothic. It is similar to the Lancet case of Regency days in Britain, and is now known to collectors as a Beehive. This example is made by William Gilbert.

Once the problem of manufacturing springs cheaply in America had been overcome, clocks were made with balances as well as pendulum clocks. This is a typical example of the Locomotive or Marine style which was made by many factories.

This is a typical movement used in
the Locomotive or Marine clock. The
escapement has the sharp teeth that were
used in old English lever watches.

A Sharp Gothic clock with eight day spring driven movement having direct drive. The paper is more concerned with advertising the firm than giving instructions. Prior to 1879.

12in drop dial by Newhaven Clock Co. These are frequently met with in Britain and it is believed that the movements were imported and the cases made here although American factories turned out similar clocks complete. Last quarter 19th century.

A miniature OG by Seth Thomas. This clock is spring driven and the type was made with eight day and one day movements. Not very common.

This clock has a similar movement to the drop dial but it is believed that cases of this type were made in Britain mostly by Italian workmen. The dummy mercury pendulum swings before a mirror.

Small timepiece marked Jerome and Co. This was after the Jerome organisation had been absorbed by the New Haven Clock Co. This clock dates from the early 1880s and shows the trend towards visible pendulums. This one appears to be combining the mercury and gridiron compensations but is in fact not compensated at all.

This timepiece combines the earlier
Sharp Gothic case with the fashion for
allowing the pendulum to be visible,
c1880.

Numerous patents are associated with
American clocks. This pendulum has an
indicator dial to show what effect on the
timekeeping an adjustment of the rating
nut would have. Not very reliable.

118

The Ansonia Clock Company of New York became famous for their imitations of French clocks. This example has a mock marble case, a visible escapement and regulation over the figure XII, but the position of the winding holes in the chapter ring indicates that it is not French.

The Greek Temple style of marble clock which was perhaps the most popular of all case designs in that material. This case really is marble but the movement is American and not French.

An American version of the Four Glass.
These clocks were made by the Ansonia
Company in many different styles and
were of a higher quality than their other
imitations of French work. The winding
holes are still in the chapter ring.

The rear view of the clock shows that a
circular movement is being used, also the
rack striking system that allows the
striking to remain in step with the hands.
The type was described in the catalogues
as Crystal Regulator.

The Ansonia movement also turned up
in cases of this type made of 'Royal Bonn'
porcelain. Early 1900s.

The last type of American clock to be
imported into Britain in quantity. Lancet
case eight day strike by William Gilbert.
Regulation is only possible by means of
the square over the 12. The pendulum
bob has no rating nut.

Many novelty 2in clocks were made by
various American firms and imitated in
Germany. This desk clock is by Ansonia.

121

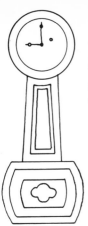

The Howard Company of Boston Mass. produced their own plainer version of the banjo which could be supplied in several sizes and was highly esteemed for offices, etc.

The Howard Company also produced their plainer version of the Girandole which corresponded with their banjo models.

A Japanese lantern type clock with single foliot. The position of the figures on the dial is adjustable to allow for the varying lengths of the hours.

The movement of the Japanese lantern clock. The design owes a lot to the Gothic clock, and it is believed that the mechanical clock was introduced into Japan by the Dutch.

Two Japanese Stick clocks. The movements are controlled by wheel balances and the time shown by the descending weight. The position of the numbers is adjustable to allow for different lengths of the hour at different times of the year.

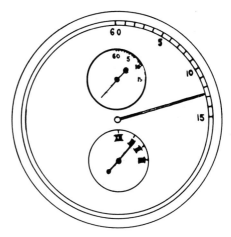

The dial of a Regulator clock. These clocks are made to give very accurate performance and the normal motion work would add resistance to the train, hence hours, minutes and seconds are shown on separate dials.

3   *Conclusion*

In a volume of this size it is impossible to deal with every variation that has evolved. Horology is such a vast subject that previously unknown types of clock are continually coming to light, and the present interest in the history of clockmaking is causing people to turn out their attics and garden sheds in the hope that something special may be found. They are sometimes lucky. The identification of such a find is often difficult, but by reading as much as possible and taking every opportunity to visit museums, auction rooms and antique shops, experience can be built up that will help to compare the new clock with others and give clues concerning its origin, together with ideas for further research.

The scheme of this book has been to trace the national differences in clock movements, remembering that there are two basic types, the plate and the birdcage, on which all others are based. With modern manufacturing methods national styles are being forgotten except in the instances where old styles are being reproduced and the idea of reproducing old styles is rapidly gaining in popularity. In Britain there are reproductions of long case clocks, Vienna Regulators, skeleton clocks and carriage clocks being made, together with a smaller number of bracket clocks, some of which have traditional movements, but many having balance controlled movements resembling those of carriage clocks.

In Holland the Stoelklok, Staartklok and Schippertje are favourite models for reproduction, some with traditional movements and others employing modern type movements made in Germany, which give themselves away by having two weights instead of the single weight supported by a pulley found on the originals. Some of the original movements of Dutch clocks have tooth profiles which are not particularly in line with modern scientific development, and so many of the reproduction movements, although in the original style, have modern tooth profiles. One firm in Veldhoven near Eindhoven, however, made a

124

speciality of producing an old type of movement using the old tooth profile, but this maker has now ceased production.

The Zaandam clock has long been popular as a reproduction item in Holland, but generally of a smaller size than its prototype and with a modern movement having two weights which, however, are in the traditional pear shape with polished brass exteriors. A Dutch firm has begun to produce wheel blanks with the 'Y' shaped crossings and other accessories for Zaandam clocks and it is hoped that the production of a full size model will follow. This is the firm of W. de Vries & Zoon, Scheen, Joure, Friesland.

Germany has a number of firms making long case clocks — makers such as Kieninger, Hermle and Urgos — but these always seem to have glass doors in the trunk which allow the pendulum and weights to be seen and this is not traditional. Other German productions include a number of Black Forest models with wooden wheels, some in kit form and others complete. The wall regulators with 'R/A' pendulums are popular, as are also the weight driven Vienna type, and even the 'Berliner' is now appearing as a reproduction. The rack clocks with a tiny pendulum before the dial have already been mentioned. German firms making replicas are Held and Selva, both of Trossingen.

France is producing replicas of the Comtoise clock although the traditional type of movement is of the later variety with the anchor escapement. Pressed brass dial surrounds, enamel dial centres and elaborate pendulums are all available and even the original type of case is being offered. Some German firms are producing Comtoise clocks which perpetuate the outward appearance but have a movement in modern style. The latest news from France is that new circular movements of the traditional type are in production, ready to be fitted with cases of the purchaser's design.

Reproduction of many American types has been going on for some time, but some of these incorporate Japanese movements running for 31 days. Particularly popular is the Schoolhouse clock or Drop Dial. The Howard Company have also reproduced their version of the Girandole which they call a 'Figure 8 Banjo'. The British firm of Biddle & Mumford (Gears) Ltd of Clerkenwell Road, London is also producing its own version of the traditional Banjo type.

Scandinavia is making versions of the 'Bornholm' and 'Swedish Farmhouse' clocks but incorporating modern style movements. In Germany, America and France it is possible to get spare parts for old clocks as a result of the interest taken in reproductions. Pendulums, weights, hands, etc are usually available. In Holland spare parts for the traditional Dutch styles can be obtained, many of which are hand-made and well match the originals.

It is necessary that a collector should be able to detect a reproduction from an original, and the only way is to acquire as much knowledge as possible by reading and seeing actual clocks. Reproduction is not a new idea; during the Second Empire many 18th-century French styles were made again and this can cause confusion. Look out also for English Lantern clocks which are spring driven. Some of these are old clocks whose movements have been replaced, possibly in Victorian times, but most of the smaller examples have been created as spring clocks with no attempt to suggest that the piece is antique.

Two types of clock which have not been dealt with in this text are now becoming popular as collectors' items. The Regulator or precision clock was intended to give results which were more accurate than those of the domestic timekeeper, in order that it might be used for astronomical observations, and the clock was also used by watchmakers for testing the performance of other clocks and watches they had repaired. In the days before radio time signals it was necessary to have one's own standard to work from and keep a check on its performance by means of observations of the sun.

The other type is the 400 Day clock with torsion pendulum which was first produced in America over 100 years ago but which became popular with German manufacturers after 1880, and is still being produced. Another American idea from the 1850s was a domestic version of a rotary pendulum clock which had been used for astronomical work. This idea was also taken up in France and, about 1973, a German firm made a number of replicas of the American model improved to go for eight days.

There have also been reproductions of specialised timekeepers, made in limited numbers, during the last few years; clocks to go by means of metal spheres which descend a kind of waterwheel; Congreve clocks where the time measurer is a steel ball that runs along a groove in a sloping metal plate which is reversed when the ball has completed one journey; and Franklin clocks where the dial has its figures in groups of three and only a single hand. With this type it is necessary to know the time to within four hours before the clock is consulted.

To assist the reader, a list of books for further study is given in Appendix II. This list could have been much longer but it has been compiled to include only those books which are believed to be still in print. Many older books are extremely useful and can often be found in

126

public libraries, especially that of the Guildhall in London, where the collections of the Antiquarian Horological Society and the Clockmakers' Company are available to the public for consultation. Many of the horological periodicals referred to contain advertisements for specialised horological booksellers who issue catalogues, which can be most useful in indicating the works available.

Membership of a society of horological enthusiasts is a great help in one's studies, and the societies produce journals which can be of considerable value as they often include matter not found in books. A list of the societies is given in Appendix III.

A list of museums is also given (Appendix IV) showing the sort of clocks that can be found there. These museums have specialised horological collections, but it is always a good plan to visit any museum that one can, because it is possible that a limited number of clocks of great interest may be found, or even only one which will repay examination. The clock lover must must always be on the alert!

Appendix I

MAKERS AND TRADE MARKS

ROBERT LÜCKHOFF ELBERFELD
20.9.00

VER. FREIBURGER UHREN-
FABRIKEN AG. INCL VORM
G. BECKER 14.5.01

A. WILLMANN & CO FREIBURG
SCHL. 3.9.01 REGLR. ETC.

UHRENFABRIK VILLINGEN 18.9.01
ALL TYPES OF CLOCK

FRIEDR. MAUTHE 14.3.02

KLING KLANG

H.A.C. 27.10.02 WECKERUHREN
MIT SCHWINGENDER GLOCKE

Gustav Becker

VER. FREIB. 16.7.03

JOHANN JÄCKLE SCHWENNINGEN
26.8.03

WILHELM GERLAND TRIBERG
15.9.03

MATTHIAS BAUERLE ST GEORGEN
3.12.03

KRONENWECKER

H.A.C. 18.2.03

VICTORIA CLOCK CIE A. MAIER
ST GEORGEN 7.5.03

GORDIAN HETTICH SOHN
FURTWANGEN 25.2.04

VER. FREIBURG 10.6.04

Silesia
VER. FREIBURG 3.10.04

Akribie

BADISCHE UHRENFABRIK 6.10.04

THOS HALLER SCHWENNINGEN
1.11.04

LUCCA

ADOLF HUMMEL SOHN.
REGULATEURENFABRIK
FREIBURG i.B. 9.11.04

The Pearl Baby

THOS. ERNST HALLER 13.1.05

Junghans

VER. JUNGHANS & HALLER 4.2.05

VICTORIA CLOCK CIE.
ST. GEORGEN 7.2.05

SCHLENKER & KIENZLE 10.2.05

Veto

VER. JUNGHANS & HALLER 18.2.05

Gold Ring

VER. JUNGHANS & HALLER 28.2.05

Bravo
JUNGHANS & HALLER 29.3.05

юнррансъ
JUNGHANS & HALLER 10.5.05

Stella
JUNGHANS & HALLER 7.7.05

**GEBRÜDER THIEL RUHLA i Th
31.7.05**

Alpha
**THOS ERNST HALLER
SCHWENNINGEN 18.12.05**

PILOT
H.A.C. 4.4.06

BADISCHE UHRENFABRIK 11.4.06

„CLOWN"
H.A.C. 15.6.06

Holla
THOS ERNST HALLER 15.6.06

Rellah
THOS ERNST HALLER 8.9.06

**JAHRESUHR SCHWENNINGEN
W. WÜRTH & CO JAHRESUHREN
26.9.06**

VER. FREIBURG 8.2.07

Quartett Gong
VER. FREIBURG 19.7.07

Harfen
VER. FREIBURG 18.7.07

Maxim
H.A.C. (WECKER) 17.8.07

„PHONOS"
H.A.C. 17.10.07

Trio Gong

VER. FREI. 24.10.07

„COPERNICUS"

HAMACHER & HAHN DORTMUND
21.9.07

„UNION"

HAMACHER & HAHN DORTMUND
2.11.07

Veni Vidi

FRIED. MAUTHE 14.12.07

META

TH ERNST HALLER 9.1.08

JOS. BÜRGER SÖHNE SCHONACH
28.1.08

Wach-auf

SCHLENKER & KIENZLE 29.2.08

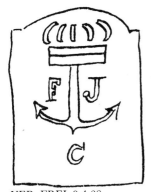

VER. FREI. 9.4.08

Haller

JUNGHANS & HÄLLER 19.5.08

Zeppelin

MAUTHE 22.7.08

Good Morning

SCHLENKER & KIENZLE 12.8.08

CAILE FERATE ROMANE

FRIEDR MAUTHE 9.10.08

SCHLENKER & KIENZLE 14.10.08

Galilei

C. WERNER VILLINGEN 26.11.08

PRAECISION

UHRENFABRIK VILLINGEN 1.12.08

Morning Glory

TH. ERNST HALLER 12.12.08

Hallerernst

TH. ERNST HALLER 13.1.09

Le Roi à Paris
SCHLENKER & KIENZLE 16.3.09

Kloxter Glocken
FRIEDRICH MAUTHE 27.3.09

Sirene
FRIED. MAUTHE 5.6.09

„Sphären"
HAC 12.8.09

„PFEIL"
HAC 18.8.09

„Colonist"
HAC 15.9.09

Jonium.
SCHLENKER & KIENZLE 25.9.09

„Ego"
JUNGHANS & HALLER 25.10.09

JOS. BÜRGER SÖHNE SCHONACH
B. TRIBERG 29.12.09

UM
UHRENFABRIK WILHELM
MÜLLER & CO MÜHLHEIM 10.1.10

Trommler Wecker
SCHLENKER & KIENZLE 6.1.10

Drummer Alarm
SCHLENKER & KIENZLE 6.1.10

Hamburg-Amerikanische Uhrenfabrik in Schramber
HAC 4.2.10

Midget
SCHLENKER & KIENZLE 11.4.10

HAC 26.4.10

132

SCHLENKER & KIENZLE 4.6.10

WART UND HÖR
WAIT AND HEAR
WAIT AND SEE

UNION CLOCK CO FURTWANGEN
22.8.10

FRIEDR. MAUTHE 12.9.10

Ergo

GEBR. JUNGHANS THOS HALLER
15.9.10

Agul

A.G. FÜR UHRENFABRIKATION
LENZKIRCH 26.9.10

Irfant

H.A.C. 28.9.10

HERMANN SCHWEIZER
SCHRAMBERG 10.11.10

Kosmos

HAC 10.1.11

„Diadem"

HAC 21.1.11

Lux

HAC 10.3.11

CYMBAL

SCHLENKER & KIENZLE 27.3.11

Mauthe

FRIEDR MAUTHE 10.4.11

ESKA

SCHLENKER & KIENZLE 12.4.11

AUTOSUN

SCHLENKER & KIENZLE 20.6.11

Schellenkönig

H.A.C. 30.6.11

Phlox

H.A.C. 30.6.11

Placet

H.A.C. 30.6.11

Timp

H.A.C. 30.6.11

Pansy

HAC 1.7.11

133

Chloris
HAC 1.7.11

Bucco
HAC 1.7.11

Fragor
HAC 7.8.11

Eclypse
HAC 5.10.11

FUCHSIA
HAC 5.10.11

JULIET
HAC 5.10.11

Fairy
HAC 5.10.11

Iwa
HAC 5.10.11

Servus
HAC 6.10.11

Sweetheart
HAC 6.10.11

Passepartout
HAC 6.10.11

Mousmé
HAC 6.10.11

Dickens
HAC 11.10.11

Mirabelle
HAC 16.10.11

Parsivalgong
HAC 28.10.11

Courier
HAC 30.10.11

Nulli—Secundus
HAC 14.11.11

Prince
HAC 22.12.11

Walküregong
SCHLENKER & KIENZLE 15.1.12

Grals
HAC 19.1.12

Amfortas
HAC 5.2.12

Klingsoe
HAC 5.2.12

Kundry
HAC 5.2.12

Titourelle
HAC 5.2.12

Kiri
HAC 12.2.12

Walhalla-Gong
SCHLENKER & KIENZLE 3.5.12

Tiefland
SCHLENKER & KIENZLE 24.5.12

Bardengong
SCHLENKER & KIENZLE 1.6.12

Arrow
HAC 15.8.12

Pfadfinder
SCHLENKER & KIENZLE 17.9.12

Divira-Gong
FR. MAUTHE 24.10.12

Joung England
SCHLENKER & KIENZLE 24.10.12

Wehrkraft
SCHLENKER & KIENZLE 2.11.12

Joung Australia
SCHLENKER & KIENZLE 8.11.12

Boy Scout
SCHLENKER & KIENZLE 30.12.12

Nonida
FRIED MAUTHE 4.1.13

„Sagittol"
HAC 24.1.13

Crescendo
JUNGHANS 31.3.13

Salvos
TH. ERNST HALLER 17.4.13

„Jung Baden"
SCHLENKER & KIENZLE 19.5.13

Jung Bayern
SCHLENKER & KIENZLE 20.5.13

Neckarwerk
SCHLENKER & KIENZLE 22.5.13
(REGULATOR MOVTS)

Waidmann's Heil
SCHLENKER & KIENZLE 6.6.13

Prior
TH. ERNST HALLER 8.7.13

Tom-Tom
SCHLENKER & KIENZLE 15.7.13

Bürk
WÜRTT. UHRENFABRIK
SCHWENNINGEN BÜRK SÖHNE
14.8.13

JAKOB PALMTAG SCHWENNINGEN
11.9.13

„Pa"
HAC 26.9.13

„Pi"
HAC 26.9.13

Isolde gong
SCHLENKER & KIENZLE 29.9.13

„Po"
HAC 10.10.13

„LU"

HAC 24.10.13

Teha

THOS ERNST HALLER 29.10.13

Bismarck

SCHLENKER & KIENZLE 30.10.13

„Drummerboy"

SCHLENKER & KIENZLE 31.10.13

„Pangong"

SCHLENKER & KIENZLE 3.11.13

„Atlantic"

SCHLENKER & KIENZLE 15.11.13

„Verna"

C. WERNER VILLINGEN 26.11.13

Von

JUNGHANS 29.11.13

Securitas

JUNGHANS 17.12.13

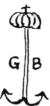

THOS ERNST HALLER 20.3.14

Jora

JUNGHANS 7.5.14

Celerina

SCHLENKER & KIENZLE 9.5.14

136

Picea

JUNGHANS 9.5.14

RUDOLF HAAS & SOHN
KARLSRUHE 15.6.14

UHRENFABRIK VORMALS
L. FURTWANGLER SÖHNE AG.
FURTWANGEN 3.10.14

WEISS BROS BIRMINGHAM REGD.
LEIPZIG 28 SEP 1875 (WEAPONS)

LENZKIRCH A.G. 26 MAY 1875

GUSTAV BECKER FREIBURG
SCHLES. 3 JULY 1875 PENDULUM
CLOCKS REGULATORS. SPRING OR
WEIGHT CASES WOOD OR METAL

H. ROPOLL 16 JUN 1876

PHILIPP HAAS und Söhne
St Georgen
Reg. 20 JUN 1876

(FOR CONTINENT WITHOUT
"TEUTONIA" WHICH ONLY FOR
ENGLAND & EXPORT)

EAGLE
"E PLURIBUS UNUM"
A DIAL and the WORDS
" TRADE MARK"
JUNHANS REGD 4 MAY 1877

137

PRODUCTIVGENOSSENSCHAFT
DER UHRMACHER VON FREIBURG
H. ENDLER & CO. IN FREIBURG
SCHLES. REG 8 OCT 1877
REGULATORS & REGULATOR
CASES

LENZKIRCH. 23 JAN 1878 ALSO
REGISTERED WITHOUT "GES.
GESCH"

LANDENBERGER & LANG IN
SCHRAMBERG 1879 (HAC FORMED
1882) THIS LABEL SEEN IN A
CLOCK WITH MONOGRAM

ON DIAL

138

GRIFFIN WITH HOLLOW
TOOTHED WHEEL

A. EPPNER & CO SILBERBURG
25 JUN 1881

BERNHOLD & SCHEURLEN IN
CANNSTATT 16 SEP 1881

L. FURTWANGLER & SÖHNE
FURTWANGEN 21 SEP 1881

JUNGHANS 3 FEB 1882 FOR CASES

PH HAAS U. SÖHNE 13 MAR 1883
BLACK FOREST WEIGHT & SPRING
CLOCKS

GUSTAV BECKER 8 DEC 1883
MOVEMENTS REGULATOR HANG
& STAND CLOCKS

UNION C.C. MERZBACH, LANG &
FELLHEIMER IN LONDON
BRANCH IN FURTWANGEN
20 MAY 1885

A GARTER WITH
TH DE GRUYTER
+ CO

HUGO KNOBLAUCH & CO BERLIN
20 JUN 1885 TRAVELLING ALARMS
YEAR CLOCKS

OSWALD MAURER EISENBACH
6 AUG 1885 CLOCKS & CASES

DURSTEN & CO DRESDEN
13 JUL 1886

ALSO 1886

CARL WERNER VILLINGEN
1 FEB 1887 COMPLETE CLOCKS

10 NOV 1887 TWO GUSTAV BECKER
MARKS RE REGISTERED
REGULATORS & MOVEMENTS

FRIEDRICH MAUTHE NEBEN DER
KRONE SCHWENNINGEN
17 AUG 1888 VARIETIES OF CLOCKS

HAC HAMBURG 10 FEB 1886
CLOCKS MOVTS & CASES

139

JUNGHANS 19 NOV 1888

JAHRESUHREN FABRIK AG IN
TRIBERG 14 JAN 1890

RUDOLF BACHRODT IN TRIBERG
4 FEB 1889 CLOCKS OF ALL TYPES

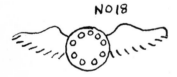

SCHLENKER & KIENZLE
SCHWENNINGEN 6 OCT 1889
REPEATED 1895 NO 18
          1897 NO 19

WÜRTTEMBURGISCHE UHREN-
FABRIK IN SCHWENNINGEN
18 OCT 1889 VARIOUS CLOCKS
REPEATED 21 MAR 1895 WITH
RICHD BÜRK INCLUDED

ANSONIA
ANSONIA CONN USA
REGISTERED LEIPZIG 11 MAR 1890

JUNGHANS 10 MAY 1890 MOVTS
CASES DIALS ETC.

MÜLLER SCHLENKER
REGULATORS SCHWENNINGEN
21 MAY 1890 TYPES OF CLOCKS

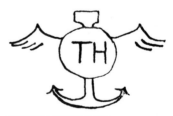

THOMAS HALLER
SCHWENNINGEN 31 JUL 1890
CLOCKS

BADISCHE UHRENFABRIK AG.
FURTWANGEN 16 DEC 1890

JAHRESUHRENFABRIK AG
TRIBERG 18 JAN 1892

H.A.C. HAMBURG 18 JAN 1892
CLOCKS REGISTERED 29 FEB 1892
ALSO FOR PARTS, CLOCKS DIALS
CASES & PARTS THEREOF

GEBRÜDER MAIER UHRENFABRIK
VILLINGEN 21 JUN 1892 CLOCKS OF
ALL TYPES

ERNST NIPPEL KOTTBUS

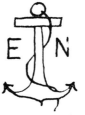

REGULATORS & ALARMS
20 OCT 1892

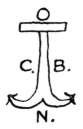

C. BÄKER NAUEN 19 DEC 1892
CLOCKS ETC

HAC HAMBURG 28 JUL 1893
CLOCKS PARTS CASES DIALS

JUNGHANS 1 OCT 1894

7 DEC 1894

UNION CLOCK CO FURTWANGEN
6 DEC 1894

L. FURTWANGLER SÖHNE
FURTWANGEN 22 JAN 1895

DUBOIS & FILS 10 JUN 1895
(GENEVA)

7 DEC 1894

*A WELL DRAWN HARE WITH
MONOGRAM BELOW*

PHILIPP HAAS & SÖHNE
15 JUL 1895

10 DEC 1894

BADISCHE UHREN FABRIK
3 JAN 1896

UHRENFABRIK VILLINGEN
MAURER PFAFF & MAIER
VILLINGEN 12 JAN 1895
REGULATORS ALARMS WALL
CLOCKS L.C. CLOCKS

THOMAS HALLER
SCHWENNINGEN 29 JAN 1896

PH. DUBOIS & FILS GENEVA
24 JUN 1896

BADISCHE UHREN FABRIK
26 AUG 1896

REGULATEUR FABRIK
"GERMANIA" FREIBURG IN SCHL.
11 DEC 1896 REGULATORS ONLY

C. ROHDE HAMBURG IMPORT &
EXPORT APL 1897

TOBIAS BÄUERLE ST. GEORGEN
20 MAY 1897

C.J. SCHLENKER SCHWENNINGEN
6 NOV 1897

*A CLUB TOOTH SCAPEWHEEL &
LEVER WITHIN IT*

J. SCHLENKER GRUSEN
SCHWENNINGEN 30 NOV 1897

*AN ELABORATE PAPER WITH
PICTURE OF A SAILING SHIP AND
AN ARCH OVER C.B IN BOTTOM
LEFT*

BADISCHE UHRENFABRIK
14 FEB 1898

SCHLENKER & KIENZLE
3 JUN 1898

HORSESHOE 2 STAR

C. WERNER VILLINGEN
21 OCT 1898

TIGER ON TREE

UHRENFABRIK VILLINGEN
MAURER PFAFF & SCHLENKER
30 NOV 1898

EAGLE HOLDING CHAPTER RING
SCHLENKER & KIENZLE
22 MAR 1899

*PADDLE STEAMER WITH WORDS
"SHIP REGULATOR"*
BADISCHE UHRENFABRIK
18 NOV 1899

*2 LIONS WITH CROWNS DIAL WITH
CROWN GB IN THE MIDDLE*
VEREINIGTE FREIBURGER
UHRENFABRIK A.G. INCL
VORMALS GUSTAV BECKER
26 FEB 1900

GERMAN EAGLE WITH GB
1 MAR 1900

GB ANCHOR & CROWN
20 OCT 1900

*ADJUSTABLE DEAD BEAT PALLETS
WITH JUF BELOW*
JAHRESUHREN FABRIK TRIBERG
22 JUN 1900

14 DAY & MONTH REGULATORS AS
WELL AS JAHRESUHREN

ALTERNATIVE TO "TIME IS
MONEY" ON 1877 JUNGHANS
TRADEMARK. MAY BE PREVIOUS
TO 1877

ON SMALL SPRING TIMEPIECE
(UNIDENTIFIED)

*FOLLOWING EXTRACTED FROM
OESTERREICHISCH-UNGARISCHE
UHRMACHER ZEITUNG 1882-6*

ERSTE WIENER PENDELUHREN
FABRIK GEBRÜDER RESCH IN
EBENSEE

AGENT ED PFEIL WIEN VII BEZ
LINDENGASSE NO 2 FROM 1.1.86
SOLOMON ABELES WIEN ALSO
AGENT

"AUSTRIA" ERSTE BÖHM
PENDELUHREN FABRIK MIT
DAMPFBETRIEB LIERSE &
GEHORSAM REICHENBERG IN
BÖHMEN

GUSTAV REISS ANNOUNCES HE
HAS TAKEN OVER CASE FACTORY
IN CONNECTION WITH ABOVE
DEC '82

OTTO STEINER UHREN FABRIK IN
WIEN & KARLSTEIN WIEN IX
WÄHRINGERSTRASSE 59

KARLSTEIN ÖSTERREICH

ERSTER KARLSTEINER UHREN
INDUSTRIE GESELLSCHAFT

JAPY FRÈRES, PIONEERS IN FACTORY
MADE MOVEMENTS IN FRANCE.

BADENIA CLOCK MANUFACTORY. J.G.
SCHULTHEISS SOHN, GÜTENBACH
BADEN. MENTIONED IN TRADE PRESS
1889. PROBABLY IN BUSINESS BEFORE
THIS. DOUBTFUL IF ANY
CONNECTION WITH BADISCHE
UHRENFABRIK IN FURTWANGEN.

145

UHRENFABRIK TEUTONIA. EARLIER
VERSION OF TEUTONIAN CLOCK
MANUFACTORY TRADEMARK WHICH
MIXES ENGLISH AND GERMAN
LANGUAGES.

THE BRITISH UNITED CLOCK
COMPANY, BIRMINGHAM 1885–1909.
THIS FIRM ATTEMPTED TO COMPETE
WITH THE CHEAP CLOCKS COMING
FROM AMERICA.

THE XC TRADEMARK SEEMS TO HAVE
BEEN RESERVED FOR THE CHEAPER
MODELS OF JAPY FRÈRES.

146

THE JUNGHANS TRADE MARK OF 1877.

G.H.S.F. GORDIAN HETTICH & SOHN
FURTWANGEN. LATE 19TH CENTURY.

THE UNION CLOCK COMPANY OF
FURTWANGEN. LATE 19TH CENTURY.

147

BADENIA. THIS LABEL IS A BEAUTIFUL EXAMPLE OF AN IMITATION OF THE TYPICAL AMERICAN LABEL OF THE TIME AS IT SHOWS A PICTURE OF THE FACTORY, AND CARTS TAKING AWAY THE PRODUCTS. THE WORDING IS ALSO IN ENGLISH.

A DIFFERENT VERSION OF THE JUNGHANS TRADE MARK OF 1877.

T & R REFERS TO THWAITES AND REED, A FIRM THAT PRODUCED MOVEMENTS FOR MANY OF THE CELEBRATED LONDON MAKERS. SERIAL NUMBERS AND DATES ARE GIVEN IN ROSE'S BOOK *ENGLISH DIAL CLOCKS*. MID 18TH CENTURY TO PRESENT.

ANSONIA CLOCK CO NEW YORK c1880–1930.

V.A.P. REPRESENTED THE INITIALS OF VICTOR ATHANASE PIERRET OF PARIS WHO EXHIBITED AT THE LONDON EXHIBITION OF 1851. THE TRADE MARK HOWEVER SEEMS ONLY TO HAVE BEEN USED BY HIS SUCCESSORS, CAILLE. CHEAPER CLOCKS.

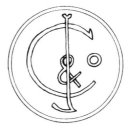

JEROME AND CO. USED BY THE NEW HAVEN CLOCK CO WHO TOOK OVER THE JEROME FACTORY, BUT MOST PROBABLY NOT BY JEROME HIMSELF.

W&H SCH WINTERHALDER AND HOFMEIER. SCHWÄRZENBACH, BLACK FOREST FROM ABOUT 1870. THE FIRM WENT IN FOR HIGH QUALITY WORK. CEASED PRODUCTION 1932.

THE NEW HAVEN CO'S OWN TRADE MARK c1880(?)–1950(?).

149

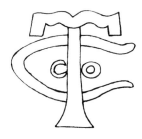

TERRY CLOCK CO, PITTSFIELD, MASS, 1880–8.

SETH THOMAS, THOMASTON, CONN. ORIGINAL FIRM FOUNDED EARLY 19TH CENTURY, NOW PART OF GENERAL TIME CORP.

WATERBURY CLOCK CO, WATERBURY, CONN. 1857–1920s.

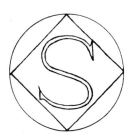

SEIKO JAPAN, 1886(?) TO DATE.

E.N. WELCH FORESTVILLE, CONN. c1880–1903.

The name of the maker of a clock is an important clue to tracing its date, but it should be remembered that the name appearing on the dial is not always that of the maker but often of the man who sold it. While many men were still making clocks by hand in Britain in the late 18th century, the tendency was increasing for parts to be obtained in a rough or half finished state and to be finished by the clockmaker concerned, or even for complete movements to be purchased and fixed to painted dials obtained from Birmingham dialmakers. The Comtoise clocks on the Continent almost always bear the name of the vendor as these clocks were factory produced in a limited area. Dutch country-made clocks are rarely signed but those from the towns usually bear the maker's name.

The late G.H. Baillie published a list of Clock and Watchmakers of the World, generally not going beyond 1825, and Brian Loomes has produced a companion volume extending Baillie's list to c1880. These two volumes between them contain some 70,000 names and there are many books published relating to towns and counties which contain still further names. As time goes on, the lists are continually being increased. A list of Dutch makers has been available for some years and a list of makers in the German speaking countries has recently appeared. The French publisher Tardy has produced a list of French makers to complement his work on French clocks, and the National Museum of Ireland has produced a list of Irish makers.

It would therefore serve no purpose to include a list of names in this present book as new ones are continually being discovered to augment the already published material. Information is not, however, readily available on the trademarks of the various factories, and so a list of these is included. Broadly speaking they begin in 1875 and run up to 1900. Some of the marks were in use before 1875 but registration generally began at that time.

The full titles of the lists of makers already published are as follows. Some of them are now out of print but they can often be found in libraries. Apart from these the following counties are being worked on at present: Dorset, Kent, Norfolk, Sussex.

Abeler, Jürgen, *Meister der Uhrmacherkunst* Published by the Author (Text in German) (1977)

Baillie, G.H., *Watchmakers and Clockmakers of the World* N.A.G. Press (1976)

Beeson, C.F.C., *Clockmaking in Oxfordshire 1400-1850* Museum of the History of Science Oxford (1967)

Bellchambers, J.K., *Devonshire Clockmakers* Published by the Author (1962)

Bellchambers, J.K., *Somerset Clockmakers* Antiquarian Horological Society (1968)

Brown, H. Miles, *Cornish Clocks and Clockmakers* David & Charles (1970)

Daniell, John, *Leicestershire Clockmakers* Leicestershire Museums (1975)

Elliot, Douglas J., *Shropshire Clock and Watchmakers* Phillimore (1979)

Fennell, Geraldine, *A List of Irish Watch and Clock Makers* National Museum of Ireland (1963)

Haggar, A.L., & Miller, L.F., *Suffolk Clocks and Clockmakers* Antiquarian Horological Society (1974)

Hawkes, A.J., *The Clockmakers and Watchmakers of Wigan* (1934)

Hughes, R.G., *Derbyshire Clocks and Watchmakers* Derby Museums (1976)

Legg, Edward, *The Clock and Watchmakers of Buckinghamshire* Bradwell Abbey Field Centre (1976)

Loomes, Brian, *Lancashire Clocks and Clockmakers* David & Charles (1975)

Loomes, Brian, *Watchmakers and Clockmakers of the World* **(Vol.2)** N.A.G. Press (1976)

Loomes, Brian, *Westmorland Clocks and Clockmakers* David & Charles (1974)

Loomes, Brian, *Yorkshire Clockmakers* Dalesman Books (1972)

Mason, Bernard, *Clock and Watchmaking in Colchester* Country Life (1969)

Moore, Nicholas, *Chester Clocks and Clockmakers* Grosvenor Museum Chester (1976)

Morpugo, Enrico, *Nederlandse Klokken en Horlogemakers vanaf 1300* Scheltema and Holkema Amsterdam (Text in Dutch) (1970)

Peate. Iorwerth C., *Clocks and Watchmakers in Wales* National Museum of Wales (1975)

Penfold, J.B., *Clockmakers of Cumberland* Brant Wright Associates (1977)

Ponsford, C.N., *Time in Exeter* Headwell Vale Books (1978)

Ponsford, Scott and Authers *Clock and Clockmakers of Tiverton* published by the authors (1977)

Reid, C. Leo, *North Country Clockmakers* Newcastle on Tyne (1925)

Tardy, *Dictionnaire des Horlogers Français* published by the author

(Text in French) (1972)

Tebbutt, L., *Stamford Clocks and Watches and their Makers* published by the author (1975)

Waters, Ivor, *Chepstow Clock and Watchmakers* Moss Rose Private Press (1978)

Clocks and Clockmakers (Northamptonshire) County Borough of Northampton Museums and Art Gallery (1966)

Appendix II

BOOK LIST

General Works

Britten, F.J., *Old Clocks and Watches and their Makers* (8th Edn) Eyre Methuen with Spon (1973)

Shenton, Alan and Rita, *The Price Guide to Clocks 1840-1940* Antique Collectors' Club (1977)

Smith, Alan, *Clocks and Watches* Connoisseur (1975)

Vogel, H. & Mühe, R., *Alte Uhren* (Text in German) Callwey, Munich (1976)

English Clocks

Bruton, Eric, *The Long Case Clock* Hart-Davis McGibbon (1976)

Edwardes, E.L., *The Grandfather Clock* Sherratt & Son Ltd (1976)

Loomes, Brian, *The White Dial Clock* David & Charles (1977)

Loomes, Brian, *Country Clocks and their London Origins* David & Charles (1976)

Loomes, Brian, *Complete British Clocks* David & Charles (1978)

Rose, Ronald, *English Dial Clocks* Antique Collectors' Club (1978)

Royer Collard, F.B., *Skeleton Clocks* N.A.G. Press (1977)

Dutch Clocks

Sellink, J.L., *Dutch Antique Domestic Clocks* H.E. Stenfert Kroese (1973)

Zeeman, J., *De Nederlandse Stoelklok* Van Gorcum (Text in Dutch) (1978)

Zeeman, J., *De Nederlandse Staande Klok* Van Gorcum (Text in Dutch) (1977)

French Clocks

Allix, Charles, *Carriage Clocks* Antique Collectors' Club (1974)

Bollen, Ton, *Comtoiseklokken* Van Dishoek, Haarlem (Text in Dutch) (1977)

Schmitt, Gustav, *Die Comtoiser Uhr* Müller Villingen (Text in German) (1977)

Tardy, *La Pendule Française* Tardy (1973)

German Clocks

Abeler, Jürgen, *5000 Jahre Zeitmessung* published by the author (Text in German) (1978)

Abeler, Jürgen, *Alt Bergische Uhren* Dr Wolfgang Schwarze Verlag (Text in German) (1969)

Bender, Gerd, *Die Uhrenmacher des Hohen Schwarzwaldes und Ihre Werke* (2 vols) Müller Villingen (Text in German) (1975 and 1978)

Edwardes, E.L., *Weight Driven Chamber Clocks of the Middle Ages and the Renaissance* John Sherrat (1976) (Also deals with other European countries)

Maurice, Klaus, *Die Deutsche Räderuhr* C.H. Beck, München (Text in German) (1977)

Tyler, E.J., *Black Forest Clocks* N.A.G. Press (1977)

Austrian Clocks

Hellich, Erika, *Alt Wiener Uhren* Callwey, Munich (1978)

Italian Clocks

Leopold, J.H., *The Almanus Manuscript* Hutchinson (1971)

American Clocks

Bailey, Chris H., *Two Hundred Years of American Clocks and Watches* Prentice Hall (1975)

Distin, W. & Bishop, R., *The American Clock* E.P. Dutton & Co Inc (1976)

Palmer, Brooks, *The Book of American Clocks* The Macmillan Co New York (1967)

Palmer, Brooks, *A Treasury of American Clocks* The Macmillan Co New York (1967)

Parsons, Charles S., *New Hampshire Clocks and Clockmakers* Adams Brown Co (1976)

Roberts, Kenneth D., *The Contributions of Joseph Ives to Connecticut Clock Technology* American Clock and Watch Museum (1970)

Eli Terry and the Connecticut Shelf Clock Ken Roberts Publishing Co (1973)

Wood jr., Stacy B.C., *Clockmakers of Lancaster County and their Clocks 1750-1850* Van Nostrand Reinhold (1977)

Precision Clocks

Erbrich, Klaus, *Präzisionspendeluhren* Callwey Munich (Text in German) (1978)

Roberts, Derek, *Catalogue of Exhibition of precision pendulum Clocks (1978)*

Appendix III

SOCIETIES AND PERIODICALS

The British Horological Institute, Upton Hall, Upton, Newark, Notts. NG23 5TE. Publication: *The Horological Journal* (monthly)

The Antiquarian Horological Society, New House, High Street, Ticehurst, Wadhurst, Sussex, TN5 7AL. Publication: *Antiquarian Horology* (quarterly)

The National Association of Watch and Clock Collectors, P.O. Box 33, Columbia, Pennsylvania 17512, USA Publication: *The Bulletin* (five times per year)

Freunde Alter Uhren, Postfach 590, 7000 Stuttgart 1, Germany Publication: *Volume of Transactions* (annual)

Association Nationale des Collectionneurs et Amateurs d'Horlogerie Ancienne (ANCAHA), 107 Rue de Rivoli, 75001 Paris, France. Publication: *ANCAHA*

Association Française Amateurs d'Horologerie Ancienne, Boîte Postale 33, 25012, Besançon, Cedex, France. Publication: *Hologerie Ancienne*

Chronometrophilia, Case Postale 313, CH 2301 La Chaux de Fonds, Switzerland. Publication: *Le Bulletin*

The American Clock and Watch Museum, 100 Maple Street, Bristol, Conn 06010, USA. Publication: *The Timepiece Journal* (annual)

There are two independent publications:

Clocks published monthly by Model and Allied Publications Ltd, P.O. Box 35, Bridge Street, Hemel Hempstead, Herts HP1 1EE

Alte Uhren (Text in German) published by Georg D.W. Callwey, KG, Streitfeldstrasse 35, 8000 München 80, Germany (quarterly).

Appendix IV

MUSEUMS

Great Britain

London

British Museum: General
Guildhall: General, with stress on the work of members of the Clockmakers' Company
National Maritime Museum: The Navigational aspect of timekeeping.
Science Museum: General, with stress on the mechanical aspect of the subject
Victoria and Albert Museum: General, with stress on the artistic aspect
Wallace Collection: French clocks

Outside London

Basingstoke: Stress on the work of local makers but some interesting items from other areas
Bury St Edmunds: The work of London and Continental Masters
Cardiff: National Museum of Wales. Clock and Watchmaking in Wales
Leicester: Leicestershire makers
Lincoln: The decorative aspect
Liverpool: General
Norwich: Bridewell Museum, East Anglia
Oxford. Museum of the History of Science: General, with attention to Oxfordshire makers
    Ashmolean Museum: Decorative, mostly 17th century and before
Waddesdon Manor, Aylesbury: French clocks

Holland

The Netherlands Clock Museum is at Schoonhoven near Gouda and exhibits not only examples of Dutch horology but also some items from other European countries. The Rijksmuseum in Amsterdam has only a limited number of horological items. At Zaanse Schans, near Zaandam, is a new horological museum which tries to show one exhibit of each type of clock. Mostly Dutch. There is a horological Museum at Frederiksord Drenthe, and the Fries Museum in Leeuwarden and the Gronings Museum in Groningen have examples of local work. The Science Museum at Leiden concentrates on the work of Christiaan Huygens.

France

Horological Collections at Besançon and The Conservatoire des Arts et Métiers in Paris. Some horology in The Louvre and the Petit Palais in Paris.

Germany

The Abeler Museum at Wuppertal has a very varied collection embracing all periods and countries. The collection at Kassel includes early clocks for astronomers and some domestic clocks. The Altes Schloss at Stuttgart contains Renaissance clocks and 17th-century work, while the Maximilian Museum at Augsburg concentrates on that City's productions. At Bamberg are clocks by Leopold Hoyss, and the Germanisches Museum at Nuremberg contains some very early pieces.

The Deutsches Museum at Munich corresponds to the Science Museum in London, and the Bayerisches Museum in the same City corresponds to the Victoria and Albert Museum. In the Bayerisches Museum there are clocks made by Leopld Hoyss.

At Furtwangen the stress is on Black Forest clocks with examples from other European countries as well and one or two pieces from America. The museum now possesses the Kienzle Collection which includes Renaissance work as well as Black Forest and other European clocks.

Triberg specialises in Black Forest clocks, and there is a small collection in the Heimatstuben at Neustadt. Schwenningen has a good Black Forest collection with some other items and is trying to concentrate on the products of the town.

Austria

In Vienna are the special Clock Museum and the Kunsthistorisches Museum, the former concentrating on Austrian work and the latter on Fine Arts. On the outskirts of the City the Geymuller Schlössl has a fine collection of Austrian clocks.

Switzerland

The Kirschgarten Museum in Basel possesses Renaissance clocks. At La Chaux de Fonds is the largest museum with the name 'Time and Mankind' where the collection is very comprehensive. Le Locle has a selection of Swiss clocks and automata. Geneva has some clocks but concentrates on watches. The Kellenberger Collection at Winterthur has a large number of Gothic clocks made by the Liechti family and some Swiss country made clocks. There are also some examples from other parts of Europe.

The Restaurant Zur Kathrin at Oerlikon displays a number of country made wall clocks. The Beyer Museum in Zürich concentrates on work of high quality.

Italy

Poldi Pezzoli Museum in Milan contains the Falck collection, which is mostly Renaissance. In the same City is the Science Museum. In Florence is the Museum of the History of Science with varied horological collection including Italian lantern clocks.

Denmark

In Copenhagen is the National Museum with Renaissance work and in Den Gamle By at Aarhus are to be found some examples of Danish country work.

Belgium

In the Musée de la Cinquantenaire at Brussels is a good European collection, small but with some Belgian examples included. A few horological pieces are in the Vleeshuis at Antwerp.

United States of America

There are a number of museums in America which contain clocks, but only a limited number can be mentioned here.

The Smithsonian Institution in Washington corresponds to the Science Museum in London and has a horological department. At Bristol, Connecticut, is the American Clock and Watch Museum (closed in winter) specialising in American products, and the Museum of the NAWCC at Columbia, Pennsylvania, possesses clocks of general interest with a large number of American examples. The Henry Ford Museum at Dearborn, Michigan, has a number of American clocks. Old Sturbridge Village, Massachusetts, sets out to portray American life in the past and includes typical clocks.

At Rockford, Illinois, is the Seth Atwood Collection which embraces a very wide field and possesses a number of high quality pieces.

In Illinois also is the State Museum at Springfield with the Hunter Collection containing clocks of various countries, and in the California Academy of Science at San Francisco is the W. Barclay Stevens Collection.

Ireland

The National Museum in Dublin contains some clocks by Irish makers and a Stoelklok.

Index of Clock Makers and Manufacturers

Maier, A., 129
Maurer, Oswald, 139
Maurer, Pfaff and Maier, 142
Maurer, Pfaff and Schlenker, 143
Mauthe, Friedr., 128, 131, 132, 133, 135, 139
Muller, Wilhelm, 132
Muller Schlenker, 140

New Haven Clock Co., 109, 115, 116, 149
Nippel, Ernst, 141
Norris, Joseph, 28

Palmtag, Jakob, 135
Pierret, Victor Athandse, 149

Ramsay, David, 23
Reiss, Gustav, 144
Rohde, C., 143
Ropoll, H., 137

Schlenker, C.J., 143
Schlenker and Kienzle, 129, 131, 132, 133, 134, 135, 136, 140, 143, 144
Schultheiss, J.C., Sohn, 145
Schweizer, Hermann, 133
Seiko, Japan, 150
Selva, 125
Shinn, Thos., 52

Steiner, Otto, 145

Teutonia Clock Manufactory, 137, 146
Terry Clock Co., 150
Terry, Eli, 43, 44
Thomas, Seth, 43, 45, 46, 47, 115, 150
Thwaites and Reed, 149
Tompion, 21, 24
Treffler, Johann Philipp, 13

Uhrenfabrik Teutonia, 146
Uhrenfabrik Villengen, 128, 131, 142, 143
Uhrenfabrik Vormals, 136
Union Clock Co., 133, 139, 142, 147
Urgos, 125

Victoria Clock Cie, 129

Waterbury Clock Co., 150
Weiss Bros., 136
Welch, E.N., 111, 150
Welch Spring and Company, 45
Werner, Carl, 131, 136, 139, 143
Willard, Simon, 43
Willman, A. and Co., 128
Winterhalder and Hofmeier, 149
Wurth, W. and Co., 130
Wurttemburgische Uhrenfabrik, 135, 140

General Index

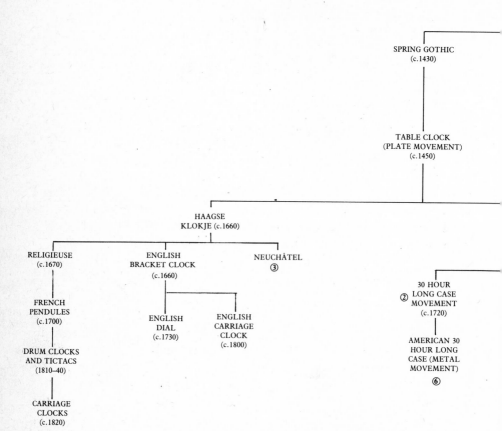

SPRING GOTHIC
(c.1430)

TABLE CLOCK
(PLATE MOVEMENT)
(c.1450)

HAAGSE
KLOKJE (c.1660)

RELIGIEUSE
(c.1670)

ENGLISH
BRACKET CLOCK
(c.1660)

NEUCHÂTEL
③

② 30 HOUR
LONG CASE
MOVEMENT
(c.1720)

FRENCH
PENDULES
(c.1700)

ENGLISH
DIAL
(c.1730)

ENGLISH
CARRIAGE
CLOCK
(c.1800)

AMERICAN 30
HOUR LONG
CASE (METAL
MOVEMENT)
⑥

DRUM CLOCKS
AND TICTACS
(1810–40)

CARRIAGE
CLOCKS
(c.1820)